RECENT DEVELOPMENTS
AND
RESEARCH
IN
FISHERIES ECONOMICS

RECENT DEVELOPMENTS

AND

RESEARCH

IN

FISHERIES ECONOMICS

Papers presented
at a Conference on
Fisheries Economics, 1965

Sponsored by the

FEDERAL RESERVE BANK OF BOSTON

Edited by

FREDERICK W. BELL and JARED E. HAZLETON

PUBLISHED FOR
THE NEW ENGLAND ECONOMIC RESEARCH FOUNDATION
by Oceana Publications, Inc.
Dobbs Ferry, New York, 1967

LIST OF PARTICIPANTS

James D. Ackert, *Atlantic Fisherman's Union*
Frederick W. Bell, *Federal Reserve Bank of Boston*
Roger E. Bolton, *Williams College*
Harold E. Crowther, *Bureau of Commercial Fisheries*
Richard M. Doherty, *Metropolitan Area Planning Council,*
    Commonwealth of Massachusetts
Vincent F. Dunfey, *Boston College*
James F. Farrell, *University of Rhode Island*
Thomas A. Fulham, *Boston Fish Market Corporation*
Frederick L. Gaston, *University of Massachusetts*
Herbert W. Graham, *Bureau of Commercial Fisheries*
Jared E. Hazleton, *Federal Reserve Bank of Boston*
Andreas A. Holmsen, *University of Rhode Island*
Harvey M. Hutchings, *Bureau of Commercial Fisheries*
Harlan C. Lampe, *University of Rhode Island*
Morton M. Miller, *Bureau of Commercial Fisheries*
Octavio A. Modesto, *Seafood Producers Association*
Darrel A. Nash, *Bureau of Commercial Fisheries*
Virgil J. Norton, *Bureau of Commercial Fisheries*
Hugh F. O'Rourke, *Boston Fisheries Association*
David A. Storey, *University of Massachusetts*
Lawrence W. Van Meir, *Bureau of Commercial Fisheries*
Roger C. Van Tassel, *Clark University*
Charles L. Vaughn, *Boston College*
Donald J. White, *Boston College*
John M. Wilkinson, *Federal Reserve Bank of Boston*

TABLE OF CONTENTS

LABOR, RESOURCE AND INDUSTRY PROBLEMS

TABLES, CHARTS, FIGURES

THE RELATION OF THE PRODUCTION FUNCTION TO THE YIELD ON CAPITAL FOR THE FISHING INDUSTRY

THE ECONOMICS OF THE SMALL TRAWLER FLEET

THE FISHING LABOR FORCE: SCARCITY OR SURPLUS?

THE OFFSHORE RESOURCES OF THE NORTHWEST ATLANTIC

THE INTERACTION BETWEEN TWO FISH POPULA-
LATIONS AND THEIR MARKETS—A PRELIMINARY
REPORT

A STUDY OF POLICY CONSIDERATIONS IN MANAG-
ING THE GEORGES BANK HADDOCK FISHERY

THE ECONOMICS OF A FISHERY: THE NEW
BEDFORD SCALLOP INDUSTRY

PREFACE

Fishing is one of New England's oldest—and most interesting—industries. Like other industries in this region, commercial fishing has undergone major changes in recent years. It still has many problems. Some are serious—all are challenging.

The papers in this volume were presented at a conference which grew out of a research study by Dr. Frederick W. Bell, Regional Economist for the Federal Reserve Bank of Boston. They present an appraisal of the industry's present position—and its potential for growth and development.

Publication of these papers is being sponsored by the New England Economic Research Foundation, a regional, privately supported, nonprofit organization created to encourage and engage in research on New England.

The Foundation is grateful to the U. S. Bureau of Commercial Fisheries and the Federal Reserve Bank of Boston, whose co-operation has made the publication of these proceedings possible.

The Foundation particularly appreciates the helpfulness of Dr. George H. Ellis, President, and Dr. Robert W. Eisenmenger, Vice President and Director of Research, Federal Reserve Bank of Boston; Mr. Harold E. Crowther, Deputy Director, and Mr. Lawrence Van Meir, Director of Economic Research, U. S. Bureau of Commercial Fisheries; and Dr. James Storer, Professor, Department of Economics, Bowdoin College, whose ideas and encouragement contributed materially to the success of this project.

The editors are grateful to Mrs. Ruth Norr and Miss Anne Pomeroy for their editorial assistance and to Miss Geneva Morrissey for her secretarial services and are especially indebted to Miss Ellen Temple for her diligent and competent work in editing galleys and page proofs.

Rudolph W. Hardy, Executive Director

New England Economic Research Foundation

RECENT DEVELOPMENTS
AND
RESEARCH
IN
FISHERIES ECONOMICS

INTRODUCTION

FREDERICK W. BELL and JARED E. HAZLETON

Federal Reserve Bank of Boston

In 1950, Donald White completed an extensive analysis of the New England fishing industry.[1] In an article summarizing the results of his research, White indicated little optimism for the long-run economic vitality of New England's oldest industry which was plagued by labor problems, foreign competition, and a dwindling resource base.[2]

In the decade and a half following White's study, many changes occurred in the fishing industry, a number of them tending to bear out his conclusions regarding its long-run potential. However, in the latter part of this period, two developments appeared on the fishing scene which, while not creating a complete revolution, certainly generated some optimism that the industry could abate or perhaps reverse the downward trend it had been experiencing for some time. These new developments were the 1964 Fishing Fleet Improvement Act offering federal subsidies for the construction of fishing vessels, and the introduction of stern trawling into the Atlantic fleet, representing the most significant change in fishing technology in many years.

---

[1] Donald J. White, *The New England Fishing Industry: A Study in Price and Wage Setting,* (Cambridge, Massachusetts: Harvard University Press, 1954).

[2] Donald J. White, "The New England Fishing Industry: America's Oldest Industry Faces Crisis," *Monthly Review,* Vol. 32, No. 3 (Federal Reserve Bank of Boston, March 1950), pp. 1-12.

Frederick Bell made a study to determine the impact of these two new developments on the future of the industry.[3] In the course of his analysis, Bell noted that while much research had been conducted in recent years on the economics of the fishing industry, the results had not been brought together in one place since the publication of White's book. Therefore, it was decided to hold a conference at the Federal Reserve Bank of Boston and to invite economists and other students of the industry to present papers on recent developments and research in fisheries economics. Over one hundred representatives of all segments of the fishing industry attended the conference, held in December, 1965. In addition, many people outside the industry, particularly representatives of electronics and defense-related research and development firms, attended because of their interest in the long-run potentialities of the sea as a source of food and exploration.

The papers included in this volume were presented at the conference. Each paper was commented upon by a person knowledgeable in the area under study. While many of the papers were oriented toward various segments of the New England fishing industry, in general the analyses are applicable to the broader topic of fisheries economics. Taken together, the papers represent an accurate appraisal of the field and indicate several areas for further research. What follows is a synthesis of the principal topics covered by the papers in this book and a brief summary of the impact of the stern trawling technology and the 1964 Fishing Fleet Improvement Act on the fishing industry..

The Demand for Fish Products

The primary market for fish products is probably one of the most competitive in the United States today. The individual fisherman can do little to differentiate his product from that of competitors. Buyers and sellers tend to be small and numerous. Furthermore, because fish must be drawn from a variable resource base, the supply to the market is subject to little control in the short run. A proper understanding of the forces shaping the market is indispensable in assessing many of the problems facing the industry.

The U.S. fishing industry is not only confronted with competition from other products such as meat and poultry, but must also com-

[3] Frederick W. Bell, *The Economics of the New England Fishing Industry: The Role of Technological Change and Government Aid.* (Federal Reserve Bank of Boston, Research Report No. 31, 1966), 215 pp.

pete with increasing foreign imports. Over the last decade, fish consumption per capita has remained stable at approximately 11 pounds, while that of competing products has increased. Per capita meat consumption has risen from about 163 to 175 pounds and poultry from 27 to nearly 40 pounds from 1955-64. Thus, fish consumption per capita is a poor third among major protein products. Moreover, domestic fishermen are supplying a much smaller share of U.S. consumption, imports of edible fish having increased from 34 percent of the total supply in 1955 to nearly 50 percent in 1964. The domestic catch has remained about constant during this period.

Darrel Nash in his paper entitled, *Demand for Fish and Fish Products with Special Reference to New England,* presents valuable information outlining the forces which affect fish consumption. Nash points out that essentially three effects have an important bearing on fish consumption per capita: *price, income* and *competing products.* On a more technical level, these effects are called the price, income and cross elasticities of demand for commodities, respectively. The special emphasis of the article is to estimate the values of these elasticities.

For all fish, Nash found the price elasticity to be well below unity indicating that a 1 percent change in the price of all fish products will result in less than a 1 percent change in the quantity of fish consumed. This means that although fish competes for the consumer's dollar, increases in fish prices do not result in a proportional shift in the consumer's expenditure to other products. Thus, fish consumption responds inelastically to changes in fish prices.

However, the price elasticity for individual fish products or species is extremely high. For example, flounder and haddock were found by Nash to have price elasticities much greater than unity thus showing that consumers freely substitute one kind of fish for another in response to relative price changes.

Price elasticity is extremely important to the industry since it reveals how gross revenue will change as a result of changes in price. If the price elasticity is greater than unity, gross revenue will increase as the price of fish products is reduced. Thus, as landings of individual species increase thereby depressing price, total revenue received for that species will rise. But Nash's research shows that for fish as a group increased production and lower prices will decrease revenue for the industry since the price elasticity is below unity.

As the consumer's income increases, food usually occupies a declining share of total expenditures. Foods, in general, are income inelastic. Nash found that for fresh and frozen fish and shellfish the income elasticity is below unity. This indicates that fish occupies a smaller and smaller percentage of the consumer's expenditures as his income increases. Fortunately, fish was not found to have a negative income elasticity which would mean that fish consumption declines absolutely as income increases. Contrary to some beliefs, fish is not an inferior good.

There are some notable exceptions to the finding that fish is income inelastic. For example, the income elasticity for groundfish is much greater than unity which means that expenditures on groundfish occupy a larger percentage of the consumer's budget as income increases. This is probably explained by what Bell calls the "fish stick revolution." [4] That is, the advent of new forms in which to market the product, such as fish sticks and dinners, has encouraged the consumer to increase his consumption of groundfish. These forms are easy to prepare and do not possess a strong fish odor. Fish sticks and dinners are made exclusively from groundfish which includes haddock, ocean perch, flounder, cod, whiting, pollock, hake and cusk.

Finally Nash treated the effects of various direct substitutes for fish products. For all fish, the cross elasticity of meat is below unity. This means that a 1 percent increase in the price of meat —due for example to a poor cattle year—results in a less than 1 percent increase in fish consumption. Thus, the consumer does substitute fish for meat when relative prices change; however, the consumer's percentage increase in fish consumption is less than the percentage rise in meat prices.

What do the various elasticities of demand mean for the fishing industry? The paper by Joseph Farrell and Harlan Lampe entitled, *The Revenue Implications of Changes in Selected Variables Examined in the Context of the Haddock Market,* deals with the implications of price elasticities for the industry. The behavior of gross revenue is especially crucial since both labor and capital usually share a fixed percentage of this revenue under a contract known as the "lay." Unlike most industries, labor must share the risks with capital of vicissitudes in weather, movements of fish populations, and changes in consumer demand.

Using a multi-equation model of the haddock market from the landing level to the ultimate consumer, Farrell and Lampe found

[4] *Ibid.,* p. 36.

that for New England haddock the price elasticity was much greater than unity. This is consistent with Nash's findings for individual species.

The authors were especially interested in the impact of changes in revenue on the rate of return on capital in the industry. They found that a 10 percent decline in landings would increase price by only 5.4 percent since the price elasticity is greater than unity. Assuming a fixed number of vessels in the industry (in the short-run) revenue per trawler would fall resulting in a decline of the rate of return on capital (net worth) from 8.7 to 5.7 percent. Thus, the rate of return would decline by 34.4 percent as a result of a 10 percent decline in landings. The effect on fishermen's wages would be almost as disastrous. The fall in wages due to changes in market conditions is more severe than that experienced by practically any segment of the American economy.

Farrell and Lampe also discuss the seasonal nature of the industry. The authors discovered that the high demand for fish during the Lenten Season produces a shift in the demand curve. They show that revenue for the industry is approximately 18 percent higher during this period. Thus, the existence of religious observances produces a rather unique influence on the fishing industry.

Vincent Dunfey in his discussion of the Farrell-Lampe paper points out that for a better analysis of the demand for fish products the market must be divided on the basis of fresh and frozen. This is an extremely important distinction since fresh fish sells for twice the price of frozen. Therefore, the New England fishing industry caters to the fresh fish market. For example, two-thirds of the haddock landed in New England is sold fresh and one-third is frozen. Domestic fishermen find it almost impossible to compete in the frozen fish market which is heavily dominated by imports.

The existence of the fresh and frozen markets produces an added dimension to the demand analysis presented by Nash, Farrell and Lampe. Frederick Gaston and David Storey in their paper, *The Market for Fresh Fish that Originate from the Boston Fish Pier Landings*, attempt to outline the marketing channels and geographical scope of the fresh fish market. This is the first research into this very important area. Using interviews, questionnaires and other techniques, the authors were able to account for the distribution of approximately 50 percent of the landings in the months of August, December and March in 1964-65.

Somewhat less than half of the identified fresh fish shipments stayed within the New England States, with most of this being consumed in Massachusetts. Nearly one-third of the fresh fish marketings occurred in the State of New York. The western part of New York was a particularly important market, with 16 percent of the total fish marketings made in the areas around Syracuse, Rochester and Buffalo. The fresh fish market was reported to extend on a geographical basis as far west as Chicago and as far south as Kentucky. Shipments of haddock, cod, pollock, and flounder did not reveal any striking differences in geographical markets as similar proportions were shipped to each region. About one-half of the fish went directly to retailers, restaurants, specialty outlets and institutions. The remainder went to intermediate wholesalers for shipment, in most cases outside Massachusetts.

The remarks made by Hugh O'Rourke, discussant for the Gaston and Storey paper, are especially interesting. O'Rourke points out that since more fresh fish per capita is consumed in New England (30 pounds per capita of fresh fish compared to about 11 for both fresh and frozen in the U.S.), the possibility of extending this high consumption to the rest of the country exists if transportation costs are lowered. According to O'Rourke, a recent study by the airlines confirms that the west coast wants New England fish products and, with air freight reduced, haddock could become a daily menu item on the coast.

The three papers presented on the demand for fish products give a thorough analysis of most of the demand factors that must be considered when studying fisheries economics.

Costs, Returns to Capital, and Technological Change

Since the fishing industry operates on a profit-sharing basis called the "lay," cost of production must be viewed differently from that for most industries. Labor cost is the most important component of total cost and varies directly with the value of the catch. Capital receives a fixed percentage of the catch out of which fixed expenses must be paid. Normally, labor must pay certain trip or variable expenses out of its share. These, in many cases, include expenses incurred in operating the vessel. Therefore, labor bears the burden of expenses which in other industries are the responsibility of management. Fixed expenses paid out of capital's share include insurance, maintenance, interest and depreciation costs.

Frederick Bell in his paper entitled, *The Relation of the Production Function to the Yield on Capital for the Fishing Industry*, presents valuable information on practically all phases of the cost of production for the fishing enterprise. Using a stratified random sample of 101 fishing firms (vessels), Bell measured the rate of return on investment (both net worth and total assets) in the fishing industry compared to other American industries.

For 1963, the rate of return (before taxes) was 1.9 percent on total assets and 5.2 percent on net worth for the entire sample. For 1962, the rates of return were .2 and 1.2 percent on assets and net worth, respectively. These over-all rates of return for the New England fishing industry were decidedly below the returns in other segments of the U.S. economy including the combined sector of agriculture, forestry and fishing, as well as manufacturing.

As is widely known, foreign imports have kept fish prices low over the postwar period. The combination of low prices and rising costs has resulted in an attrition of factors of production from the industry. In groundfishing, the number of vessels and fishermen drastically declined, presumably due to low wages and return on investment. However, any industry in decline may have sectors which are still viable. Thus, Bell attempted to identify which characteristics or segments of the fishing industry make rates of return comparable to other, more viable industries of the U.S. economy.

Some segments of the New England industry apparently earned a fair or competitive return on investment. Bell found that the rate of return was significantly related to vessel size. The five groups with the highest rates of return in the sample were all over 60 tons while the lowest five groups were under 60 tons. Moreover, the five leading groups were engaged in groundfishing which is reported to be a depressed segment of the industry. No clear relation was found between age of the vessel and the rate of return. Approximately 93 percent of the difference in the rate of return between large and small vessels was due to the superior income-generating power of the bigger vessels. Large vessels spend many more days at sea per year and attract more competent and experienced captains.

Using data from the random sample, Bell developed a Cobb-Douglas production function for the fishing firm showing the relation between landings and inputs of capital and labor. One notable feature of this function is a shift variable which represents the greater utilization of factors of production by larger vessels. The analysis revealed that capital, labor, and the utilization variables were all important determinants of output (landings).

Bell's findings that fishing vessels are subject to "economies of scale" are important because they reveal sectors of the fishing industry which may yield a competitive rate of return on investment.

For example, large groundfish vessels which cater to the fresh fish market yield rates of return comparable to U.S. manufacturing industries. The importance of the fresh fish market was discussed in conjunction with the paper by Gaston and Storey.

Contrary to Bell's findings, Andreas Holmsen discovered that the operation of a small trawler is a profitable enterprise. However, in his paper on the *Economics of Small Trawlers* discussing the profitability of the Rhode Island fleet, Holmsen employed depreciation figures different from those normally stated on profit and loss statements and drew his sample of vessels from a fishing cooperative. In his study, the rate of depreciation was determined by asking the owner how long he expected to keep the vessel and, assuming a constant price level, what he thought the vessel would be worth upon resale. For 46 vessels in the sample, the return (before taxes) on net worth was 14.1 percent in 1964. This rate of return, according to Holmsen, compares favorably with that obtained in many manufacturing industries. Furthermore, the sample was divided into high and low earning vessels. The analysis revealed that the differences between groups are not in the nature of the equipment, but in the management. Size, age or value of the vessel was found to have no significant effect on the returns to capital. Holmsen recommends that what is needed is not larger vessels, but a fleet of small (70-90 feet), powerful trawlers and good shore installations.

The studies by Bell and Holmsen, while differing in findings, give an accurate account of costs and earnings in the fishing industry under existing technological conditions. Without a major change in technology which would increase productivity, the U.S. fishing industry has faced steadily rising costs in the postwar period. Consequently, the absence of significant productivity increases has contributed to a deterioration in the international competitive position of the U.S. industry.

An important new technological innovation which may raise productivity is the stern trawler. All New England fishing vessels except for two newly-constructed ones are side trawlers. As the name implies, on a side trawler fishermen set and retrieve the nets from the side of the vessel. In contrast, on stern trawlers the net and gear are operated from the stern. The main difference between the two is the manner in which the net is handled and this determines the construction design of the vessel.

Stern trawling has gained wide acceptance among Canadian and European fishermen. At an international stern trawling conference in 1964 at Grimsby, England, the majority of delegates were convinced that this was the method of the future.[5] Moreover, the results of experiments conducted by the Department of Fisheries of New Brunswick, Canada, showed that stern trawlers were more seaworthy and allowed more rapid handling of the net.[6] Moreover, because only half as much time was needed to handle the net on a stern trawler, it was possible to make more complete hauls in a normal fishing day. As a result, stern trawlers were on the average able to catch 20 percent more fish per trip.

In an earlier study, Bell compared the performance of the *Narragansett*, New England's first stern trawler, with that of a control group of side trawlers.[7] The results of the statistical tests indicated that the stern trawling technique made a significant difference in productivity between the *Narragansett* and the control group. The *Narragansett's* average catch per trip was more than 70,000 pounds, about 29 percent higher than the average for the side trawlers. In addition, the *Narragansett* needed only seven men in the crew as opposed to an average of nine on other vessels. Stern trawlers may cost up to 20 percent more since shipbuilders are unexperienced in the construction of such vessels; however, the increased productivity and reduced crew needed for the stern trawler are more than adequate to offset the higher construction costs. Bell estimated that the rate of return (on net worth) would be 14.3 percent for the stern trawler compared with 8.7 percent for the side trawler. The comparison suggests that the stern trawler with its more than 20 percent increased productivity and other cost savings would be a more profitable investment unless its construction costs were at least 40 percent greater than the side trawler's.

This technological advance may have an important bearing on future costs in the fishing industry. In addition, stern trawling may reduce the hazards in the industry while at the same time its increased productivity would raise wages and the return on capital above current low levels.

Labor, Resource and Industry Problems

Along with capital, labor has experienced difficulty in earning a competitive rate of return for its services. Thus, it has been difficult to attract highly competent fishermen to the industry.

---

[5] United Kingdom White Fish Authority, *Stern Trawling*, edited by George Ward, (Fishing News [Books] Ltd., May 1964).

[6] H. W. Stern, *A Comparison Report of Stern vs. Side Trawling for the Province of New Brunswick, Canada.* (Unpublished report, 1964).

[7] Bell, *op. cit.*

In their paper, *The Fishing Labor Force — Scarcity or Surplus*, Morton Miller and Virgil Norton attempt to explain the past behavior of the fishing labor force and to assess future market conditions for this factor of production. Pointing to the failure of labor productivity in the fishing industry to keep pace with advances in other segments of the economy, they stress that the lag in fish harvesting technology has led to a reduction in the number of fishermen and to an increase in the differential between fishermen's wages and the average wage for male workers in all industries.

The decline in both employment and relative wages in the fishing industry is shown to be consistent with the theory of short-run behavior in a declining industry. The older workers are apparently trapped, while their younger, more mobile counterparts escape into expanding industries, where both employment and wages are increasing. Thus, the declining industry must relax hiring standards as relative wage scales are further depressed by the lower marginal productivity. The authors drew on a study they made of the Boston offshore trawler fleet to support their contention that the fishing industry, like any declining industry, tends to attract or retain the residual in terms of education, training, and skills.

Looking to the future, Miller and Norton warn that the fishing industry faces serious manpower shortages in both skills and numbers. They conclude that the industry must look to new labor force entrants to fill the gap between the available fishermen and the industry's labor requirements. However, recruitment of additional fishermen can only occur if earnings improve to levels more comparable with the national average. This in turn requires an increase in production efficiency coupled with the introduction of new technology and upgraded skill requirements. It would seem that the rapid introduction of the new stern trawler might help to alleviate the problem of low efficiency.

In his comments, James Ackert introduces the problem of the wide range in earnings of individual fishermen resulting from the dispersion of productiveness among the different vessels in the fleet. Since fishermen's wages are tied through the "lay" to the earnings of the boat, fishermen employed on the newer, more productive boats earn substantially more than their counterparts on the less productive, older vessels. Thus, average wage levels may be somewhat deceptive when used to judge the attractiveness of the fishing industry. This is particularly important because new entrants into the fishing labor force must serve on the marginal vessels to gain experience before they can obtain a berth on a newer, more productive boat. This compounds the problem of attracting younger men to the industry.

The commercial fisheries of the world rest on the productive capacity of a series of organic populations. Thus, the resource base is a third factor of production in addition to capital and labor. Because the industry is tied to a natural resource, the problems are more complex and difficult.

Herbert Graham in his paper, *The Offshore Resources of the Northwest Atlantic,* painstakingly defines the resource base for the Northwest Atlantic Fishery, taken to be the continental shelf between Rhode Island and Greenland. This area, traditionally fished by New England vessels, comes under the jurisdiction of the International Commission for the Northwest Atlantic Fisheries (ICNAF).

As Graham points out, increased fishing effort by European countries has markedly increased production from the North Atlantic, but the catches of U.S. vessels have held steady or declined. As a result of the increased fishing effort, the point has now been reached where many stocks are producing at their maximum sustainable level. These include the much prized stocks of cod, herring, haddock, and sea scallops. Graham estimates that, considering all stocks, present total landings are probably within 20 percent of the total sustainable tonnage.

Viewing the resource from the standpoint of a national competitor, the fisherman sees that the only means of increasing landings is to expand fishing effort. However, if all competitors expand their fishing effort, the result may well be a decline in total landings as the maximum sustainable yields for various stocks are exceeded.

In his comment on Graham's article, John Wilkinson begins by making the important distinction between the concepts of optimal economic output and maximum physical output. In this regard, he stresses the need for additional information on the costs of expanding the resource base as well as on sustainable yields for various stocks. As an alternative to competitive exploitation, Wilkinson suggests cooperative management of fisheries.

A prerequisite to proper fisheries management is a thorough understanding of the interrelationships between the biologic and economic aspects of commercial fisheries. This is the subject to which Harlan Lampe turns in his intriguing paper, *The Interactions between Two Fish Populations and Their Markets—A Preliminary Report.* Lampe's paper extends the analysis made by others of the interaction between an isolated fishery and its market. His model considers the stability of, and the stability conditions necessary for, two independent fisheries cojoined by two mutually dependent markets. By linking the demand functions of the two fish species, he is able to develop a dynamic model of the cobweb form and to investigate the oscillatory path to equilibrium under differing parametric values.

Lampe demonstrates that the time required to achieve stability in a two-fishery model considerably exceeds the time required for an isolated fishery with identical characteristics. Thus, the problem of fisheries management appears to be much more complex than was indicated by the earlier static forms of analysis of a single fishery and its market. Changes in market conditions resulting in changes in fishing effort are shown to have a long lasting effect upon population levels. Finally, Lampe shows that the speed of adjustment as well as the equilibrium levels attained is a function of both the population and market characteristics.

Among the changes in Lampe's model suggested by Harvey Hutchings in his discussion is that the model be expanded to consider the case of dependent fish populations as well as dependent markets. This would appear to be a useful extension of the model given that fish populations quite often prey upon one another or depend for food upon the same common organism. While Hutchings cautions that the data required for estimation of the parametric values in models such as the one presented by Lampe may be difficult to obtain, he stresses the importance of such models in helping to solve the problems of fisheries management.

Once a decision has been reached by the participants in a fishery to join in managing the exploitation of their common property resource, the problem remains of implementing the proper policies to achieve their objectives. Lawrence Van Meir, in his paper, *A Study of Policy Considerations for Management of the Georges Bank Haddock Fishery*, explores the policy alternatives open to planners in drafting programs of fishery management.

Applying his analysis to the case of the Georges Bank haddock fishery, Van Meir demonstrates that if this fishery continues to be competitively exploited, it is likely that total fishing effort will eventually exceed that which allows the maximum sustainable yield of the resource. Consequently, unless fishing effort is somehow regulated, the consumer is likely to be faced with the prospect of less haddock available at higher prices. Thus, one policy goal indicated is to curtail fishing effort at the level required to maintain the maximum sustainable yield.

Van Meir considers three means of achieving this policy objective. First, it may be decided to permit free entry into the fishery. Given this decision, successful limitation of total tonnage to the maximum sustainable yield would require the imposition of a quota system applied to total tonnage. However, Van Meir notes that this solution could lead to accelerated exploitation by individual participants resulting in a short fishing season, lower average prices for haddock, and increased costs.

Turning to a second policy alternative, Van Meir considers monopolistic exploitation of the fishery which would imply obtaining the maximum net revenue above the costs for labor and capital. This solution would lead to a level of effort below that required to produce the maximum sustainable yield. Van Meir rejects this solution on the grounds that it would be contrary to public policy elsewhere in the economy.

Finally, Van Meir suggests that a third policy of achieving the maximum employment of labor and capital at going rates of return for these inputs might be established by placing quotas on fishing effort. These units of fishing effort could than be licensed out to fishing firms until the total quota was exhausted. Each individual participant would be free to purchase or sell his fishing rights. Thus, the more productive boats could afford to purchase the rights of the less productive boats.

In his comments, Thomas Fulham questions Van Meir's assumption that a fishery management program must be the sole province of the Federal government, suggesting that a better alternative might be cooperative management by the states and the Federal government. As a boat owner, Fulham is understandably concerned about the prospect of a fishery managed under a quota system. In this regard he questions the quota system favored by Van Meir, pointing out the difficulties inherent in any attempt to define a unit of fishing effort.

The problems confronting the different segments of the U.S. fishing industry are perhaps nowhere better illustrated than in the case of sea scallops. Donald White and Charles Vaughn in their paper, *The Economics of a Fishery—the New Bedford Sea Scallop Industry*, update their earlier analysis of the New Bedford sea scallop industry.[8] Their findings indicate that this segment of the fishing industry has continually lost its share of the market to Canadian

[8] R. M. Doherty, G. P. Draheim, D. J. White and C. L. Vaughn, "Economic Study of Sea Scallop Production in the United States and Canada," *Fisheries Industrial Research,* Vol. 2, No. 3, (Washington: U.S. Government Printing Office), 1965.

imports during the past decade.

The primary reason for the loss of this share is more favorable conditions for capital and labor in Canada. The Canadian Government, through a program of low interest loans, accelerated depreciation allowances, and outright grants, has encouraged the construction of a fleet of new fishing vessels. At the same time, the lack of unionization of the Canadian fishermen permits vessel owners to reap many benefits not available to their American counterparts. Canadian vessels operate at sea for longer periods of time and sail with more men aboard thus increasing manpower per unit of capital. Finally, the "lay" under which Canadian fishermen work is much more favorable to the vessel owners. Although both the Canadian and the U.S. segments of the industry have been confronted by a decline in the productivity of the scallop resource base in the period since 1962, the Canadians have continued to increase their share of the U.S. market.

One factor peculiar to the industry has been the promotional program financed by the New Bedford Seafood Producers Association to strengthen the sea scallop market. The program has been credited with stimulating demand for scallops and maintaining revenue in the face of a decline in output. White and Vaughn recommend that this program might well serve as a model for other segments of the fishing industry.

The Future of the Fishing Industry

The future of the fishing industry is heavily tied-in with government legislation. Under a law passed in 1792, the purchase of fishing vessels constructed outside the United States is prohibited. Unfortunately, vessels constructed in this country cost about twice as much as those built abroad. To compensate the fishermen for this difference, the Congress passed, in 1964, the Fishing Fleet Improvement Act which makes available subsidies ranging up to 50 percent of U.S. construction cost for fishing vessels.

A study by Bell indicated that for New England as a whole, the Fleet Improvement Act may reverse the decline in the fleet and stabilize the region's share of the market.[9] The new technology of stern trawling, encouraged by the construction subsidy, will help to raise productivity, while providing increased safety for the crew and higher wages. These new developments will offset some of the advantages of foreign competitors although they will still have lower

[9] Bell, *op. cit.*

labor costs and greater proximity to some fishing grounds. As a result the rate of return on investment in the fishing industry may reach a competitive level and induce an inflow of capital. At the same time marginal trawler operations will be eliminated at a faster rate as a result of lower fish prices.

In the long run the economic vitality of the U.S. fishing industry will depend on its ability to modernize the fleet. If realized, the result will increase returns, to both capital and labor and provide somewhat lower prices to the American consumer.

This forecast is not without qualification. Harold Crowther in his paper, *Our Fishing Industry in the World Race—A Straggler or an Awakening Challenger,* discusses the possibility that these forecasts will materialize against the background of the many problems which face the U.S. fishing industry today. It is with this paper that the conference opened.

OUR FISHING INDUSTRY

IN THE

WORLD RACE:

A STRAGGLER OR AN

AWAKENING CHALLENGER?

HAROLD E. CROWTHER

Bureau of Commercial Fisheries

In looking over the agenda for this conference, I noticed the names of several individuals who have spent most of their lives in the fisheries. In fact, I recognize a few who were well entrenched in the fishing industry when I first worked in Boston over 25 years ago. If at that time those of us in the fisheries had tried to look 25 or 30 years into the future, would we have predicted the industry as it is today? Actually, I believe some predictions would have been fairly accurate, for generally the changes over this period have been gradual. But one thing is certain today: whichever way we go in the *future* the changes will not be gradual. In this era of rapidly developing technology, our fishing industry must move forward or be overrun.

I will not attempt to predict what is to come, but I would like to talk about some of the factors that may affect the future of the industry. To do this, let us take a look at the fisheries through the eyes of two appraisers, one a pessimist and the other an optimist. These types of individuals are not entirely fictitious for I am sure each of us has talked to both kinds at one time or another about our fisheries.

The Pessimistic View

When asked how things are going in the fishing industry, the pessimist is likely to predict that the industry is living on borrowed time. To prove this point he will cite some of the problems he considers to be particularly grave.

Resource Problems

His first claim will be that in recent years we have had serious declines in some of our resources, or at least the fish are not available to our vessels. For example, in 1965 we saw a drastic decline in menhaden along the Atlantic coast; ocean perch landings have declined to such a degree that there is only a limited fishery left; scallops are not as abundant as in years past; the whiting resource has been hard hit by non-U.S. fishermen; and many of our oyster beds have been decimated—just to name a few on the east coast.

Foreign Fleets

Off our coasts, sometimes almost within sight of land, vessels of foreign countries now range in great numbers over fishing areas we once considered our own. The size of these vessels dwarfs our ships and at times more than 1,000 of them are off our coasts competing for the resources we need now or will need in the future. According to reports many more vessels of other nations are expected to join the present fishing fleets. During the past year the area from Georges Bank to the Grand Banks, for example, was fished by nearly a score of nations, including such newcomers as Poland, Rumania, and East Germany. To make the situation worse, most of these fleets are partially or wholly subsidized by their governments.

Imports

Imports of fishery products are increasing day by day and even now about 60 percent of our supply of fish and shellfish comes from abroad—and at prices which are difficult to match. This year for the first time it appears that more than one-half of the *food* fish consumed in the United States will be imported. Also, there are tariff negotiations in process which the industry feels could result in lower duties for foreign products.

Other Protein Products

In addition to competing in the market with foreign products, our fishing industry faces severe competition from domestic foods, such as poultry which now retails for the unbelievably low price of less than 30 cents per pound.

Pollution

Every day our rivers, bays, inlets, and other estuarine areas become more and more polluted by domestic and industrial wastes which rob the waters of oxygen and threaten to destroy many species of fish and shellfish which spend at least a part of their life cycle in these areas. In addition to general pollution, pesticides are creating a serious threat to many of our fishery resources. Concentrations of only a few parts per billion of some pesticides can be toxic to the larvae of some fish and shellfish. Even now pesticides are present in most of our inland and coastal waters. One of the problems is that these marine animals tend to concentrate the pesticide in some of their body tissues. Therefore, very small amounts in the water can be built up to concentrations which are harmful to the fish and shellfish.

Per Capita Consumption

In spite of efforts to increase consumption of fishery products, the per capita consumption of these products has risen very little over a period of years. It still ranges between 10 and 11 pounds and there appears to be little chance of any major increase in the demand for fish and shellfish.

There are other problems the pessimist could cite, but at this point he has almost convinced himself and his audience that the future for fisheries is indeed dim.

The Optimistic View

But, there are always two sides to a story. Although the pessimists outnumber the optimists, there are still those persons possessed with a positive attitude who firmly believe that this industry has a great future—and they have arguments they believe will prove it.

New Resources

It is estimated that off the coasts of the United States lie unutilized fishery resources which can supply about 15 billion pounds of fish annually—about three times as much as we now catch. And beyond our coastal waters, where we should be fishing more, are resources far beyond the level we now harvest. As proof of this, one has only to look at world catches of fish and shellfish in the last 25 years. In 1940 the world catch was about 45 billion pounds; in 1950, 44 billion pounds; in 1960, 84 billion pounds; and in 1965, over 100 billion pounds. In contrast, the United States catch in 1940 was 4.8 billion pounds; in 1950, 4.9 billion pounds; in 1960, 4.9 billion pounds; and in 1964, 4.5 billion pounds. In essence, we have stood still since 1940 while catches throughout the world more than doubled. The fish were there—we just did not catch them.

Dr. William M. Chapman of the Van Camp Seafood Company made some interesting calculations in a recent paper he presented. "The ocean is able to provide about 400 million tons (880 trillion pounds) of animal protein, in forms suitable for harvest and use by presently known means, most of which dies and returns to the web of life in the ocean." I would like to point out that Dr. Chapman does not refer to the species of fish we now catch but to animals which are lower in the food chain. He further calculates that 24 million tons of this usable animal protein is required in the diet of about 3 billion people, the present population of the world. Even if the world population increased 10 times its present size, only 240 million tons annually of the 400 million tons available would be required. If these figures are correct, the oceans are certainly a greater storehouse of food than most of us have been able to visualize in the past.

Fish Protein Concentrate (FPC)

Those, like our friend the pessimist, who do not want to believe that there are abundant unutilized resources would say, "Even if this were true, what would you do with the fish you caught, since we are having trouble marketing our present catches?" The optimist has a ready and realistic answer—fish protein concentrate.

One of the most exciting accomplishments in recent decades is the development of this highly nutritious concentrated protein powder which can be made odorless and tasteless, and which is resistant to spoilage in any climate from the tropics to the Arctic. Its nutritive qualities are so great that as little as 10 grams (1/3 of an ounce) per day added to a deficient vegetable diet will supply a balanced diet.

FPC is essentially whole fish with practically all of the oil and water removed. Although usually thought of as a white powder, it can be produced as a paste or in other forms with a variety of flavors ranging from beef bouillon to cheese. One manufacturing process, using one species of fish, the Atlantic red hake, has been worked out by the Bureau's laboratory at College Park, Maryland. The only problem remaining is to get the approval of the Food and Drug Administration to manufacture fish protein concentrate for human consumption from whole fish. This is now under consideration by Food and Drug.

Per Capita Consumption

While it is true that the per capita consumption of edible food fish has remained between 10 and 11 pounds for a number of years, this is not the full story. Harold Cary of Van Camp Seafood Company recently pointed out that overall fish consumption has not remained static. In the past the housewife purchased and used whole fish or dressed fish, only part of which was consumed. Now the trend is to convenience foods which are usually 100 percent edible fish. The remainder of the whole food fish is normally converted to fish meal during processing. Also, industrial fish such as menhaden and other species are converted to fish meal, which is used for production of poultry and eggs. According to Mr. Cary's calculations, the per capita consumption of all fish (live weight basis) in the United States is now about 63 pounds. He also states that, based on these figures, the consumption of fish has increased at just about three times the rate of the population increase.

Increased Demand

Whether per capita consumption increases or not, an increased demand for food fish, as for all foods, must come in the future as the population explosion continues. It is predicted that the population in the United States in the next few years will increase to at least 225 million persons. If the per capita consumption remains at about 11 pounds this would require an additional 385 million pounds annually just to satisfy the population increase alone.

Increased Knowledge of the Resources

Much remains to be learned about the resources which our industry fishes, but each year we are learning more and more about those
off our coasts as well as the distant water resources. In time, as we
learn more about the requirements of fish, their habits and their
behavior, we will be able to accurately predict in advance whether
certain species will be abundant or scarce, and where and when they
will appear. With some species the predictions are already being
made, and with considerable success. In time we can also look to
the establishment of fish farming and the culture and growth of
shellfish in land-based plants.

Exports

While the United States is the world's leading importer of fish,
its exports traditionally have been limited. But this situation appears
to be changing. Exports in 1964 increased 13 percent over 1963. Another encouraging sign is the increased demand for fishery products
in Europe. This new market should in time help reduce exports to
the United States and offer a promising market for United States
fishery products.

Within the past few months the United States fishing industry
participated for the first time in foreign trade fairs. The results were
very encouraging and indicated that United States products have a
large potential market in Europe if we wish to go after it. We have
just learned that one of the United States participants in the world
trade fair has received an order which was large enough to clear out
the entire supply of the product on the west coast.

Curb of Pollution

Pollution of United States waters is far from under control, but
the problem at long last is now receiving attention at the highest
levels. Drives to control the dumping of wastes and to clean up rivers
and bays are under way and will intensify. Also, the dangers of
unrestricted use of pesticides are under careful review and it is possible that curbs on the methods of using pesticides will be put into
effect. This is a difficult problem but one which the United States
recognizes it must solve.

Congressional Activities

Within the past few years and especially during the last 2 years, Congress has shown that it recognizes and is willing to be responsive to the needs of the fishing industry. The 88th Congress and the first session of the 89th Congress have been very productive. For example, the new construction differential subsidy act has recently become law. United States vessel owners can now build their vessels at a cost comparable to that of foreign vessels, or nearly 50 percent less than they were paying before the act was passed. This is encouraging the construction of modern, efficient vessels.

Other legislation provided for an extension of the Fishery Loan Fund, a $5 million program for Federal aid to states, a pesticide research program, and other measures helpful to the industry.

New Gear

New developments with fishing gear give promise of opening up entirely new fisheries. For example, the new midwater trawl now under test by the Bureau has been successful in catching up to 60,000 pounds of Pacific hake in a 30-minute tow. Other promising gear and improved methods of detecting fish are now being tested.

With newly developed instruments, it is possible to position a trawl exactly where the fish are, at any depth between the bottom and the surface. Instruments in the pilothouse tell the captain where his trawl is located. We are finally progressing to the stage where we are not fishing blindly. Electronic equipment has given us eyes, but as yet we are still nearsighted. However, I predict that as electronic equipment improves we will be able to detect schools of fish quickly and then harvest them at a lower cost.

The optimist could cite many other developments which would seem to point out a bright future for the United States fishing industry, but the examples given should provide some hope, even to those who are the most skeptical.

Which Direction?

The average person will realize that it is not wise to consider only the dark or only the bright side in predicting the future for fisheries. All factors, good and bad, must enter into the decision. But there is one factor which we have not discussed and it is perhaps the most important of all—the human element.

Almost every one of the items I have mentioned as contributing to the pessimistic or optimistic side are controlled one way or the other by man. Resource failure is perhaps an exception, and even that will be under man's control at some time in the future.

The point I am trying to make is that the direction the United States fishing industry takes from this point on is up to groups such as this—and to individuals such as you. If even a fraction of the people in New England associated with the fishing industry determined that the industry in this area was to move ahead, it would do so. There are several examples within your own area which help to prove this point. The Fisheries Loan Fund came into being in 1958 because a group in New England became concerned enough with the desperate financial position of many trawler owners to see that action was taken. When the story was brought before Congress and enough interest was shown by the New England industry to convince Congress there was a need, the Loan Fund was enacted into law. Since 1958 a total of 198 loans totaling more than $5 million have been made from the Loan Fund in the New England area.

It is no secret that Congress attempts to carry out the will of the people, but the Congressman must know what the people want. If the industry is uninterested, the Congressman will be the same. Also, if he finds his constituency cannot agree, he will be very reluctant to take action because it would place him in the untenable position of being in the middle between groups of his constituents.

I do not mean to imply that the solution to your problem lies solely in the Congress itself. Congress may help but the real effort must come from industry itself. If the industry can define its problems and make a concerted effort to solve them, it will succeed.

In the past year or two many of us in the Bureau have noticed what appears to be the beginning of a rebirth of the New England fishing industry. I will not mention names, but at least a part of this is due to just a few people in New England who felt that the industry had a future and set out to prove it. So far they have shown they were right.

Another recent development is further evidence that others believe the industry in New England has a future. Under the new construction differential subsidy program—a large, 262-foot stern ramp trawler is to be built. If this is successful, others undoubtedly will follow. To a large extent the future of the New England industry depends on the confidence all of us have in the fishing industry.

This conference on New Developments and Research in Fisheries Economics, which the Federal Reserve Bank of Boston is sponsoring, is a symbol of that confidence. It is a credit to the Federal Reserve Bank of Boston that they have undertaken to hold this conference, for it demonstrates a desire on their part to understand the problems of industry. The two articles written by Dr. Frederick Bell which project hope for this industry will also help a great deal in instilling confidence into the New England industry.

In summary, I will admit that the fishing industry of the United States faces problems, as does any other mature industry, but there can be a bright future ahead. Whether or not the industry takes the road toward that bright future depends on groups of leaders such as you. The dream of all of us in the Bureau of Commercial Fisheries is that you in New England will unite into a group with a common goal and that this movement will spread throughout the country. Hopefully, in time we could have the industry speaking with one voice. When this happens I predict we will be well on the way to assuring that the United States fishing industry is a formidable challenger in the race for the ocean's resources.

DEMAND FOR
FISH PRODUCTS

DEMAND FOR FISH AND FISH PRODUCTS
WITH SPECIAL REFERENCE
TO NEW ENGLAND

*DARREL A. NASH**

Bureau of Commercial Fisheries

When a product is placed on the market, how will it fare with respect to the amount the consumer will purchase and the price he is willing to pay? How will consumers react in terms of quantity purchased to a change in the price charged for a product? How can the industry know if a lower price for its product will result in increased or decreased total revenue? What effects will changes in the rest of the local and national economy have on the price and quantity purchased of this product? These are some of the important questions an industry must answer for efficiency in marketing of its product.

One of the first steps in finding answers to these questions is to obtain an understanding of the economy in which these products are marketed. The following information is important for fishery demand analysis. Per capita disposable personal income in the U.S. has increased at an average of about 1.5 percent per year since 1955 when adjusted to account for the effects of inflation. Personal expenditures for food are increasing also, but make up a smaller proportion of consumer income each year. In 1955, food expenditures were nearly 22 percent of personal disposable income. By 1964, this had declined to slightly more than 18 percent.

*This paper is based upon research done by the author for the Division of Economics, Bureau of Commercial Fisheries, USDI. Valuable comments and suggestions were received from several of the staff of the Division including Drs. Harvey Hutchings, Virgil Norton, and Fred Olson. The contents are the responsibility of the author.

During this period there has been a considerable upgrading of the American diet. An increasing part of the diet is being made up of protein rich foods. While the per capita consumption of all food has declined from 1,480 pounds per year in 1955 to 1,420 pounds in 1964, per capita consumption of meat and poultry has increased considerably. Per capita meat consumption has gone from about 163 to 175 pounds and poultry from about 27 pounds to nearly 40 pounds from 1955 to 1964. Fish, however, has not shared in this increase—the per capita consumption has remained at approximately 10.6 pounds per capita throughout this period.

Fish products have fared better with respect to per capita expenditures. Per capita food expenditures excluding alcoholic beverages have increased by 15 percent since 1955. Meat expenditures, per capita, have increased 21 percent, poultry by 4 percent, and fish by 18 percent. It should be pointed out that these expenditure figures have not been adjusted for inflation. The major increase in per capita expenditures for fish may be explained by two factors, inflation and the increased catch of higher valued species.

Domestic fishermen, however, are supplying a much smaller share of this consumption—imports of edible fish having increased from 34 percent of total supply in 1955 to nearly 50 percent in 1964. Domestic catch has remained about steady during this period. The increased total consumption in the U.S. has been due to an increase in the population.

To obtain answers to the questions posed, methods for measuring the behavior of consumers need to be used. This is the purpose of consumer demand analysis. No one, of course, pretends to be able to explain totally, or even in large part, the behavior of consumers. Experience from commerce, together with the development and testing of economic theory, have determined several economic factors or variables affecting consumer demand.

When the typical man on the street speaks of demand, he is generally referring to a given price and a given quantity of a particular item. That is, if we talk about the demand for cars, the man on the street would generally think of the present quantity being sold at the present price. However, when an economist speaks of demand, he is thinking of something more. That is, how much of a given commodity an individual or group of individuals will purchase at various prices. It is generally assumed that an inverse relationship exists between quantity demanded and price. That is, the higher the price the lower the quantity purchased and the lower the price the higher the quantity purchased. The sum of all individual demand for a commodity is known as the market demand or total demand. There are other factors which affect this quantity-price relationship. These are called determinants of demand. A determinant of demand is any factor which tends to alter the price-quantity relationship, that is, increasing or decreasing consumption at a given price. Thus, an increasing demand means that consumers are willing to buy more at each possible price than they were previously, or conversely that they are willing to pay more for a given quantity. A decreasing demand means just the opposite. Consumers will now take the same quantity only at a lower price, or will take less at the given price.

There are several major determinants of demand. The most easily understood is population. As the population of our society increases, more consumers are added to this society and we would expect demand to increase, meaning that more of most items would be purchased at each possible price.

The second important determinant of demand is income. As individuals in our society become wealthier, they are able to purchase more goods and are able to upgrade their purchases to higher quality and more luxurious items without lowering consumption of other goods. Thus, purchasing power, which is dependent on prices in relation to income, is very important. In general, in our society, incomes have been going up faster than the prices of the goods and services that consumers buy.

Another important determinant of demand for a particular item is substitute goods. As the prices of substitute goods change, this in turn influences the consumption of a particular item. For example, as the price of coffee increases, we might expect consumers to buy more tea. Likewise, as the price of poultry decreases, we might expect people to consume more poultry and fewer items such as beef and pork.

Therefore, in demand analysis, what we attempt to do is to determine the various quantities that consumers are willing to purchase at different prices and to isolate the effects of changes in population, income, and prices of other goods on these price-quantity relationships.

The reason it is necessary to have a clear understanding of these relationships is because in our empirical research we need to separate out just how much of a change in a dependent variable, say quantity purchased, is due to each of the independent variables, such as price, consumer income, price of competing goods, or other

variables, such as size and characteristics of the population, inflation, or maybe some unknown factors. [1]

In expressing the relationship of prices to consumption or the
effects of population, income, and prices of other goods on the
price-quantity relationship of a particular good, we use a term
called elasticity. Price elasticity is consumer responsiveness to price
changes. It is important from an industry standpoint to know something about the price elasticity of a particular good because it indicates what will happen to total revenue when the price and/or quantity changes. As stated above, in general, as price goes down, quantity tends to go up, and as price goes up, quantity tends to go down.
The real question is, with respect to total revenue, as price goes up
does quantity decrease more or less than enough to offset this increasing price? If the decrease in quantity more than offsets the
increase in price, total revenue will go down and demand is said
to be elastic with respect to price. If the decrease in quantity is
less relative to the change in price, total revenue will go up and
demand is price inelastic. Thus, we are very interested in knowing
whether an item is price elastic or inelastic.

Income elasticity is also important, because it shows what
happens to quantity purchased of a good as income changes, other
things being equal. If income and quantity purchased of a particular good move up and down together, the income elasticity is positive. The larger the income elasticity, the greater will be the change
in quantity purchased of a product with a given change in income.
The purchase of most goods, of course, increases with increases in
income. However, for some products less is purchased at a higher
income; thus these are termed inferior goods.

The expression of the relationship between the change in the
price of one good and the resulting change in consumption of another good is called cross elasticity. The cross elasticity tells us
the percent by which the consumption of tea, for example, is expected
to change with a given percentage change in the price of coffee.

All of these elasticities are important because an industry needs
to know the expected change in consumption of its product as
prices, incomes, or prices of competing goods change by a given
percent.

---

[1] A dependent variable is one which is influenced by other variables in the system.
An independent variable influences the dependent variable or variables and is
not influenced by them. In demand analysis, price and/or quantity are dependent variables, while consumer income, prices of substitutes, and other movements of the general economy, which influence demand, are independent variables.

With this background, I would like to tell you about the work in demand analysis we are doing in the Division of Economics of the Bureau. There have been very few results of demand analyses for fish products published to date. When other studies are conducted, particularly independent projects, the consistency of results can be checked.

For our work, demand equations have been prepared for about 20 fish products classified by type of fish and type of processing. Seven of these items are products of New England fisheries. In addition, certain other equations such as demand for all fishery products should be of interest to this group.

At this time, our work must be in the form of a progress report. The results must be accepted as tentative because the studies are not completed. The results we have obtained are from market data, commonly called time series data because they are aggregated data for a population and derived through time. A second source of data which we have obtained, but have not fully analyzed are consumer budget data collected from a consumer panel by Michigan State University. These are called cross-sectional data as they are from individual families in a short time period.

The majority of the equations used have been linear.[2] This means that graphically the estimated demand curve will be a straight line. In the most recent run, some logarithmic equations were included. Log equations express directly how the percentage changes among dependent and independent variables are related. An advantage of using log equations, cited by some analysts, is that elasticities may be obtained directly from the regression coefficients. I think more appropriate tests should be (1) desirable results from the statistical analysis, that is hight t and F values; high correlation coefficients, (2) results which confirm theoretical expectations—in sign and magnitude, and (3) success in forecasting. Also, a price elasticity which changes, i.e., is more elastic at higher prices, has more intuitive appeal to me than the constant elasticity which is obtained from log equations. Still, the final test should come from the above criteria.

Several trail runs have been made on each product class with a number of different variables included and various alternative deflators used, such as the consumer price index for all items, the consumer price index for food, and some wholesale price indices.

---

[2] Single equation least squares regression analysis has been used so far in our work.

The purpose of deflating is to adjust the price and income data in order to take inflation into account. This is done by dividing prices and income by a price index.

The results have not been entirely satisfactory so far. Many of the regression coefficients have not been found to be significantly different from zero.[3] However, in those cases where statistically significant results were obtained, these are fairly consistent and in general have the expected sign and magnitude. The major interest in this work is in obtaining estimates of the elasticities explained previously.

Now to consider some of the results of our work. The price coefficient using linear equations for the demand for all fish and shellfish products is not significantly different from zero. Thus, we could not compute the price elasticity. By use of log equations, a price elasticity of approximately −.45 was found. This compares with an estimated price elasticity for fish of −.65 made by G. E. Brandow of the Pennsylvania State University.[4]

An elasticity coefficient of −.45 means that when the price of fish changes by 1 percent, the quantity purchased will change in the opposite direction, as indicated by the negative sign, by .45 percent. As pointed out previously, with a demand which is price inelastic, when the quantity of fish and shellfish purchased increases, other things being equal, total revenue will decrease because the relative increase in quantity is less than enough to offset the price decrease. Conversely, if the quantity of fish and shellfish purchased decreases, total revenue will increase because in this case the decrease in quantity is not sufficient to offset the price increase.

A price elasticity of −.45 for all fish and shellfish may seem somewhat low; however, other results as reported below tend to support this figure. In general, products with more substitutes have a higher price elasticity. Thus, we expect that the less aggregated the data we are working with, the more substitutes and thus the higher will be the price elasticity. This is shown by the following case.

From linear equations we obtained a price elasticity of about −.50 to −.55 for fresh and frozen fish and shellfish for the average price and quantity of 1948 to 1963. For the 1962-63 price and quan-

---

[3] The regression coefficient is simply the number of units that the dependent variable changes for a unit change in the independent variable. Thinking graphically, it is the slope of a line.

[4] G.E. Brandow, *Interrelationships Among Demands for Farm Products and Implications for Control of Market Supply.* Pennsylvania University. Agricultural Experiment Station Bulletin 680, August 1961.

tities, an elasticity of about −.70 to −.75 was obtained. As these figures show, the price elasticity for the less aggregated item, fresh and frozen fish and shellfish, is higher than for the more highly aggregated item, all fish and shellfish. It is expected that price is more elastic at higher prices than at lower prices. For example, the price elasticity for the 1962-63 period is higher than that for the average price and quantity. Prices for fresh and frozen fish and shellfish have been increasing through time.

I would like to be able to report on canned fish in order to compare this to fresh and frozen fish, however, we were not successful in obtaining significant regression coefficients for this product.

Moving to individual products, we have analyzed the demand for fresh and the demand for frozen flounder fillets. Fresh flounder fillets show a price elasticity from about −4.0 to about −6.0 for the average price and quantity for the years 1950 to 1963. Contrary to expectations, the price elasticity here was higher at low prices than at high prices. We would expect the price elasticity to be higher than for all fish or for fresh and frozen fish and shellfish as a group, because the opportunity for substitution of an item such as flounder fillets is quite high. Frozen flounder fillets show an elasticity of about −3.5 for the average quantity and price for the years 1954 to 1963. Again, elasticity is higher for lower prices than for higher prices.

The difference in price elasticity between fresh and frozen flounder fillets may seem somewhat puzzling. However, it could well be that a considerable difference in markets for the two products exists. Frozen fillets have the advantage of a much wider market area than do fresh fillets. The advantage in revenue appears to be with fresh fillets however. A price reduction of fresh flounder fillets by 1 percent can be expected to increase consumption of fresh flounder fillets by 4 to 6 percent, while a similar price decrease for frozen flounder fillets is expected to increase quantity by 3.5 percent.

Note that price elasticity is considerably greater for these individual products than for the aggregated items. Again, it is felt that the major reason for this is the greater opportunity for substitution in the case of the individual products.

The price elasticity for fresh and frozen haddock fillets is estimated at −1.4 for the average price and quantity for the years 1954 to 1964. The equation resulted in a higher elasticity at higher prices than at lower prices as we expected. This elasticity coefficient is, of course, considerably lower than that of the two flounder price elasticities. It is difficult to explain a difference this great, although part of it may be because both fresh and frozen haddock fillets are included in the same equation, and the flounder products are separated.

For each of these products, the price elasticity is found to be greater than one. This means, if these estimates are correct, that total revenue in these fisheries will be increased by increasing the quantity sold of these products. Total revenue, however, is not the same as net profit. Thus, the availability of the resource and the costs of production, manufacturing, and marketing also must be used in deciding upon expansion of these fisheries.

Less success was obtained in estimating income elasticities for these fishery products. Even when these results were significant, the range of elasticities was quite wide for the different solutions obtained. In general, higher elasticities were obtained for deflated incomes than for undeflated incomes. For fresh and frozen fish and shellfish the income elasticity was estimated to be in the range of 0.65 to 1.00. For the groundfish products, the range was from 2.50 to 5.90. These figures show the percent by which the quantity of fish consumption will increase for a 1 percent increase in income.

The unexpected occurred, however, with frozen flounder fillets in that income was not significant, while for fresh it was highly significant. These results must be verified or rejected by further research.

From the income elasticities obtained, our preliminary conclusion is that consumption of fish products, while it will increase with increasing income, will no more than keep pace proportionately with income increases and probably will increase less than proportionately. For certain individual products, such as fresh flounder fillets, consumption may increase proportionately faster than income.

Various substitutes were included in the demand equations depending upon the product under analysis. For all fish products, the cross elasticity for meat was in the range of .35 to .60. This means that for a 1 percent increase in the price of meat, consumption of fish is expected to increase by .35 to .60 percent. For fresh and frozen fish and shellfish this value ranged from .55 to 1.40.

A cross elasticity coefficient between quantity purchased of fresh flounder fillets and the price of frozen flounder fillets was found to be in the range of 1.4 to 2.3. It is interesting to see the cross elasticity between meat price and fresh flounder fillets is not significant, indicating that meat is not an important substitute for flounder fillets, but is for all fish combined. It is to be expected, that for fish as a group, meat is an important substitute but is not for individual fish products.

A higher cross elasticity, that is 2.9 to 4.3, was found between the price of all fish and quantity purchased of fresh flounder fillets than the cross elasticity between price of frozen flounder fillets and quantity of fresh flounder fillets. This indicates that all fish combined is a closer substitute for fresh flounder than are frozen flounder fillets. This result can certainly be questioned. The cross elasticity between the price of all fish and the quantity purchased of frozen flounder fillets is estimated at about 1.6, somewhat lower than the same figure for frozen fish.

From the results of our demand studies available so far, the general conclusion can be made that, from the standpoint of consumer demand, the New England fisheries can expect to profit by increasing production of flounder and haddock fillets because demand is price elastic. It is to be expected that the other groundfish species also are price elastic. An independent study has estimated an elastic price for ocean perch.[5] Also, with a positive income elasticity, the increasing consumer income can be expected to increase revenue to the industry.

If the primary producers are to share in this, however, the dilemma of high production costs must be solved. If these costs are lowered, profits will increase even if production does not expand. If any significant expansion is to occur, production costs must be lowered to a level allowing domestic producers and manufacturers to compete successfully with imports.

With the rapid pace of our economy and the occasional rapid changes in consumer choice, such as for fish steaks and dinners, demand analysis will be as difficult or more so in the future than at present. Retailers are moving toward merchandising to suit the individual or distinct consumer groups. An extensive survey for food chains has just been completed to determine what these consumer groups are likely to demand in terms of food and services.[6] The demand analyst must take account of these characteristics if he is to be successful in his work.

By the same token, producers and manufacturers of fishery products should keep abreast of this and similar studies to inform

[5] Joseph Francis Farrell, *Market Models of Selected New England Fish.* (unpublished Master's thesis), University of Rhode Island, 1964.
[6] "Consumer Dynamics in the Super Market," *Progressive Grocery.* (The study was reported in issues of the magazine in 1966.)

themselves of the developing consumer preferences for fish products in the several varieties and forms of processing. The same forces making demand analysis more difficult, also make it more important for industry to utilize the information which can be derived from demand analysis in their planning and decision making.

COMMENT

ROGER E. BOLTON*
Williams College

The bulk of Dr. Nash's paper deals with elementary concepts in demand analysis, which we all accept as important. I shall therefore confine myself to commenting on a few specific points and on the importance of further work in this area, some of which Dr. Nash already promises us his shop is undertaking.

I must say at the outset that I bring very little prior information about the fishing industry to my task, so I must confine myself to comments from a general theoretical and econometric outlook.

One general feature of the paper may be a shortcoming. When one talks of the demand for fish "with special reference to New England," one must focus on demands which cause derived demands for the factors of production in that area. However, the paper deals almost exclusively with the demand for all fish, whether imported or caught domestically. This is important as a first step, but perhaps we should have heard a little more on the role of imports in the market. Dr. Nash does say their share in the total supply is large and rising. But his discussion of competing products, cross elasticities, and so forth does not stress the role of imported fish as a competing product for domestic fish. We are told about, and given empirical results about, the cross elasticity of demand for fish with respect to meat, and for one type with respect to another, but it would have been good to stress that the highest cross elasticity of all may exist for domestic with respect to imported fish. Of

*At the time of the conference, I was Instructor in Economics, Harvard. Since then I have become Asst. Prof. of Economics, Williams College.

course, market adjustments may be so rapid that the two relevant prices are perfectly correlated, making the independent effects of the price of imports impossible to establish statistically. It would be helpful to know, although most at the conference may already know, whether imports are generally limited to certain species or processed forms, in which case some of the results presented may permit assessment of the cross elasticity with imports after all.

A more fundamental point relates to the so-called "identification problem." Dr. Nash does not ignore this plague of all demand analysts, and reveals an intention to estimate more general market models which allow for simultaneous relationships. However, I feel he should have given more caveats on his single equation results than he did.

It is well known that a simple time series regression of observed quantities on observed prices can easily produce a function with a slope much different from the true demand curve, even if one assumes the observed points are equilibrium ones. By true demand curve I mean a price-quantity demanded function which holds in the real world, subject only to some random shifts, the average effect of which is zero but which can be substantially plus or minus in any particular period. Although income and population are often introduced in demand functions to remove some of the systematic shifts in the curve, some random shifts may obviously remain. Economic theories are never good enough to apply exactly, and it is the task of econometrics to specify just what kinds of errors are probable.

With such shifts in the demand curve, some bias in estimation is almost inevitable with least-squares single equation models. How much bias depends on a number of things.[1] One is the relative stability of the demand curve as compared to the supply curve; another is whether, and with what sign, the shifts in the demand curve are correlated with the shifts in the supply curve. Without detailed specification of these it is simply impossible to tell whether the estimate

---

[1] General references on this subject are: M. A. Girschik and T. Haavelmo, "Statistical Analysis of the Demand for Food: Examples of Simultaneous Estimation of Structural Equations," *Econometrica,* Vol. 15 (April 1947), pp. 79-110, reprinted in part in W. C. Hood and T. C. Koopmans, eds, *Studies in Econometric Method* (John Wiley, New York, 1953), pp. 92-111; E. J. Working, "What do Statistical 'Demand Curves' Show?", *Quarterly Journal of Economics,* Vol. XLI (1927), pp. 212-235, reprinted in American Economic Association, *Readings in Price Theory* (Richard D. Irwin, Chicago, 1952), pp. 97-115; and R. J. Foote, *Analytical Tools for Studying Demand and Price Structure,* Agricultural Handbook No. 146, U.S. Department of Agriculture (U. S. G. P. O., Washington, 1958), pp. 53-56. The first of these sources employs algebraic arguments, the latter two graphical ones.

of the function's slope is accurate even apart from sampling variability. In other words, the bias will be unknown even if an infinitely
large sample of experience is available and has been tabulated. This
fundamental ignorance is the essence of the "identification problem,"
and is reflected in the question Working used to title his famous
article nearly 40 years ago.

Demand analysts in agriculture have come to cope with this
problem by making various assumptions, allowing the bias to be
measured in the sense that its expected value can be determined.
Assume for a moment that the shifts in the two curves are not correlated, i.e., that the random factors which shift the demand curve
are independent of those which shift the supply curve. If we express
the true demand function with quantity as the dependent variable,
and if the true slope is negative, the least squares estimate of the
slope will be higher, in an algebraic sense, than the true slope. If
the estimate is still negative, this means its absolute value will be
less than the true one. But the bias may be so great that the estimate will be positive even if the true slope is negative. This approaches the extreme result mentioned by Working—the analyst sets
out to estimate the demand function but winds up getting an estimate of the supply curve.

However, it can be shown that the bias of a very large sample
will be quite small if the demand curve is very stable relative to the
supply curve. In the limit, if the demand curve is perfectly stable
and doesn't shift at all, the least-squares estimate of quantity on
price will give the exact slope of the true function. Given any size
of the variance in the random shifts for demand, the least-squares
bias is reduced as the variability of the supply curve is increased.
And given the sizes of both variances, the less sensitive supply is
to current price, the more accurate the estimate of the demand
curve. In fact, if the supply function is perfectly inelastic with
respect to current price, the demand function estimate is correct if
price is used as the dependent variable in the equation.

If we abandon the assumption that the shifts in the two curves
are not correlated, the bias can be predicted only if we specify the
sign and extent of the correlation. Working showed that a positive
correlation in the shifts tends to bias upwards the estimate of the
elasticity's absolute value. A negative correlation between the shift
factors does the opposite. If income effects are not removed, we
might expect a negative correlation, because rises in income shift
the demand curve to the right and the supply curve to the left,
assuming a booming economy opens up new opportunities elsewhere

for the resources in the fishing industry. Using income as a separate independent variable obviously helps remove such influences.

All these considerations point up the need to work with a complete model of the market, including both supply and demand theories. The case for single equation models is not hopeless, however. As I said, agricultural economists have justified the assumptions necessary to believe that the estimated elasticity is in fact reasonably accurate. If the demand curve is assumed to be stable, and the supply curve definitely not, and if independence is assumed, we are not in bad shape. And these may be very plausible assumptions. Stability of the demand curve is increased greatly by including income as an independent variable and thus removing its systematic effect on the price-quantity relationship. And the supply curve may fluctuate a great deal due to vagaries of weather, or to the cobweb cycle, or other factors. Another helpful assumption, that supply is inelastic, is also widely held. What I want to say is that I missed such specifications in Dr. Nash's discussion of fish. I unfortunately do not know enough about the industry to offer much information. It does appear, however, sufficiently different from growing wheat to raise some doubts. A very inelastic supply curve may be plausible on some grounds, but not on grounds of a long lag between production and market offerings.

In commenting on Dr. Nash's empirical results, I am at a handicap because the discussion is not very specific. That may be proper for what is a progress report, and not a finished analysis. But I would have preferred to have the specific equations presented in the paper, including some of the ones for which significant results were not obtained. Dr. Nash did not mention what level of significance he used, so it would have been helpful to have the standard errors themselves, since one might want to apply different levels. To get more technical, it would of course have been interesting to know about the residuals from the equations. The Durbin-Watson statistic, so important for time series work, and a brief commentary on the pattern of residuals and any extreme ones are what I have in mind. The Durbin-Watson statistic would have been helpful in assessing the standard errors, since the standard errors may be biased downward even when the coefficients themselves are not.

I can only applaud the plans revealed here for further research. Dr. Nash is certainly on sound ground in anticipating various statistical difficulties, including multicollinearity and simultaneity problems. His use of the Michigan consumer panel data should produce interesting results, but he is wise to warn about the differences in interpretation of cross-section coefficients as compared to time series ones.

In conclusion, I feel Dr. Nash and his colleagues have embarked on a fruitful study and one that should be of importance to the New England fishing industry and to those interested in demand analysis generally.

THE REVENUE IMPLICATIONS OF CHANGES IN SELECTED VARIABLES EXAMINED IN THE CONTEXT OF A MODEL OF THE HADDOCK MARKET*

*J. F. FARRELL and H. C. LAMPE***

University of Rhode Island

Introduction

The purpose of this paper is to assess the revenue implications for the New England fishing industry of various changes in several variables. The emphasis on gross revenue stems from the fact that the relationship of revenues to workers' incomes is much closer in an industry where risks are intimately shared both by force of contract and tradition. In addition to assaying the potential impact on revenue of changes in a single variable, one can also obtain perspective on the relative importance to revenue of different variables. Due to limitations of space a small number of alternatives has been examined; a sufficient number, however, to indicate the utility of a model in making certain evaluations.

The basis of the results has been taken to be 1963-64; the time is only important where dollar amounts are given. The percentage figures are, in most cases, directly deducible from the model. These relations were obtained from a model that has been developed within the the past two years.[1] This investigation will be limited to only certain of the equations of the model.

*Contribution No. 1178 of the College of Agriculture, University of Rhode Island.
**Instructor and Associate Professor, respectively, of Food and Resource Economics.
[1] This model and its formulation is described in "The New England Fishing Industry: Functional Markets for Finned Food Fish I and II." Economics of Marine Resources papers Nos. 2 and 3, University of Rhode Island, 1965, by these authors. Copies are available on request.

To place the model in perspective, a review of its development is necessary. The main objective of the model was to provide estimates of the demand for the haddock products of the New England fishing industry at the various levels between the fishermen and the national consumers. To fulfill a secondary objective, an effort was made to isolate and demonstrate seasonal changes in demand for this species.

The model consisted of ten equations wherein the functional relations of the major determinants of supply and demand were formulated. Since there was mutual dependence of variables within and between equations, reflecting what were believed to be the conditions in the industry, the parameters of the equation system were estimated using "limited information, maximum likelihood" methodology. Parameter estimates were obtained for whole-year and for half-year periods, the latter in order to isolate the observed increase in market activity during the first half of the calendar year (including the Lenten period).

The existence of five market levels in what may be termed, loosely, the New England fishing industry, was postulated as a basis for the five pairs of demand-supply relations. These five levels are: 1) the *landings or dockside markets.* Here fishing units dealt with first-buyers, the wholesaler-processors. Since the preponderance of the catch is processed, emphasis was placed on processing; wholesaling of whole fish for retail sale as such was assumed to be negligible. 2) the *wholesaler-processors.* At this level there was a broadening of demand reflecting the alternatives available to processors in their purchases; that is, they were not limited to the dockside market but could import or draw from cold storage. These alternatives were formalized as two additional markets; 3) the *cold storage market,* since movements of holdings over the annual period clearly indicated manipulation by holders to take advantage of shifts in demand, and 4) the *imports market.* Although there were indications that a substantial portion of imported products originated from branch plants of U.S. firms, the flow of these products was assumed to be directly competitive with the domestic regional industry. There was considerable evidence that the major exporter to the region was Canada, with some additions from other extra-national sources. Consumer demand, finally, was represented in 5) the *retail market,* from which demand throughout the system was derived.

The development of appropriate data series was a major problem. Limitations in series representing wholesale movements and imports and in various price series such as import prices and wholesale prices led to the poor results in the "middle market" area, particularly in the equations dealing with storage, imports and wholesaling functions.

Observations were drawn from the nine-year period, 1954-1962. Monthly data resulted in 108 observations. This, in effect, precludes comment on the interesting weekly variations in demand seen in the haddock fishery, particularly in the fresh-fish market, but does permit analysis of seasonal changes in demand.

In general, the model was strong in the landings-market equations, somewhat less so in the retail equations, and weak in the middle market area. The difficulties here were associated principally with three variables. These were: 1) the *wholesale price* of frozen and of fresh haddock fillets. The wholesale price was clearly identified in the sources as a price paid by wholesalers in the primary markets of Boston, Gloucester and New Bedford. It was assumed, however, that it would be equally relevant as a price received by these agents. 2) the *net market movement*, a surrogate variable which represented the wholesale quantity supplied. Net market movement consisted of landings plus imports, plus or minus monthly changes in cold storage holdings as appropriate. The net market movement variable was not a reliable measure of wholesale trade since trade and sales took place without a net disappearance as in the retail area. 3) the *cold storage holdings* are measured by the last-day-of-month stocks. The net change in cold storage is the difference between two end-of-month stocks. The holdings variable does not adequately reflect actual movements in and out which would have been more useful.

The parameters of the haddock model are to be found in Appendix I.

Reliability Tests of the Model

To test the reliability of the landings market demand equations over a period not covered by the model, data for the years 1963-1964 were obtained for the variables used in the model. Parameters of the (whole year) equation tested were as follows: (all following equations in natural logarithms) [2]

---

[2] The coefficient of elasticity may be obtained from these parameters by taking their reciprocals.

$$Y_1^a = 2.8727 - .450448Z_1 + .773113Z_9 + .390029Y_3$$

[a] Where Y_1 was the weighted average New England landings price of haddock, Z_1 the quantity of haddock landed in New England ports, Z_9 the wholesale price of frozen fillets of haddock at three major ports in the region, and Y_3 the weighted average New England landings price of "all fish" (defined below).

The landings price for haddock was estimated using the 1963-64 values of all other variables. The computed price was extraordinarily close to the actual weighted average monthly ex-vessel price of all haddock landed in New England ports in 1963-64. This correspondence is shown graphically in Figure 1. The correlation of the two series produced an r^2 of .97. Hence, the landings demand equation for haddock was believed to be quite reliable and useful.

A further test was made using extreme values of landings and prices to determine if over this range the model proved equally effective. For this purpose, the demand for haddock and the demand for "other" fish were related as they are in fact coupled in the model equations.[3] Parameters of the (whole year) equation tested were as follows:

$$Y_3^a = 4.9798 + .397090Y_1 - .316785Z_4 - .072375Z_3$$

[a] Where Y_1 and Y_3 were as defined above, Z_3 the cold storage holdings of "other fish," and Z_4 quantities of "other fish" landed in New England ports.

It would appear that if one takes extreme conditions, distortions in the model might well appear. The actual maximum-minimum values of monthly haddock landings in the past two years were, respectively and in thousands of pounds, 17,526 and 4,213. The associated minimum price for the same two-year period was 5.22¢/lb., and the price given by the model is 6.12¢/lb. For all fish the real minimum price was 4.65¢/lb. and the model gives a price of 4.91¢/lb.[4] These tests suggest that, at least at the producer level, these equations may well permit evaluation, with reasonable validity, of the impact of changes in pertinent variables.

---

[3] Those food fish which comprise over 75% of the catch—cod, flounder, ocean perch and pollock.

[4] All fish were represented by cod, cusk, flounder, white hake, haddock, ocean perch and pollock. One may suspect correlation between this series and the haddock price series. Tests showed r^2 to be $-.114$ between the two series.

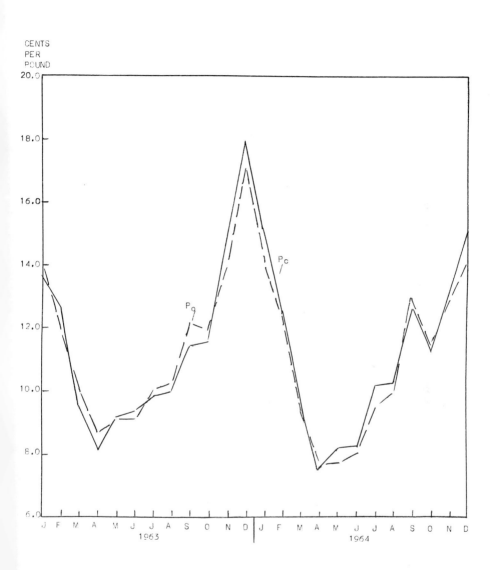

FIGURE 1. Actual (Po) and Computed (Pc) Haddock Prices, New England, 1963-1964.

Five hypothetical situations will be posed and their effect on gross revenue measured. The years 1963-64 will be employed in the analysis.

Whole Year Results

One of the reasons for creating the model was to enable assessment of impact of potential changes in the industry. To this end, consider the effect on price and/or income that could be expected from certain kinds of changes. These remarks are confined to the landings market. It should be understood that they are made for the fleet as a whole and cannot be applied to individual boats. Where the individual boat is concerned, these changes could have much greater, much smaller, or no impact whatsoever; that is, they are average outcomes, given various changes.

If a decline in haddock landings were to occur in consequence of long-term factors such as an increase in fishing intensity in Georges Bank, gross revenue to producers would decrease. This follows directly from the fact that demand at the ports for fish is highly elastic. If the decline in landings were 10%, on the order of almost one million pounds per month (on the average), the magnitude of the decline would be about 5.4%, or $1,313,775 for the New England total gross revenue from haddock computed over the years 1963-64.

The impact of a decline in landings on net profits to boat owners would be more significant. Using Dr. Frederick Bell's statement of net worth based on a 1964 sample of the New Bedford fleet, a decline of net profit of 34.3 percent, with the rate of return to net worth falling from 8.7 to 5.7 percent, would result from a 10 percent decline in landings.[5] While the "shared cost of operation" was changed in the same proportion as the change in the catch, precise estimates are not possible because, among other things, the items carried under "fixed expenses" were allowed to remain constant. These figures, however, give an indication of the approximate magnitude of the decline. Details of the computation, including the effect on stern trawlers, are in Table 1.

---

[5] Frederick W. Bell, "The New England Fishing Industry—Part I, A New Technology," *The New England Business Review*, August 1965, (Federal Reserve Bank of Boston), Table 4, page 9.

TABLE 1

**EFFECTS ON GROSS REVENUE OF A 10% DECREASE IN
NEW ENGLAND HADDOCK LANDINGS,
BASED ON DATA FOR 1963-64** [1]

	Conventional Side Trawler		Stern Trawler	
	Data from Source	With 5.4% decrease in G.R.	Data from Source	With 5.4% decrease in G.R.
Investment				
Equity in first year	$ 63,230	No change	$ 74,750	No change
Revenue				
Value of catch (28 trips)*	$160,000	$151,360	$192,000	$181,632
Less shared cost of operation	9,658	8,692**	11,130	10,017**
Net revenue	$150,342	$142,668	$180,870	$171,615
Less crew share (64% of N.R.)	96,219	91,308	115,757	109,834
Vessel share	$ 54,123	$ 51,360	$ 65,113	$ 61,781
Fixed expenses	46,054	No change	49,432	No change
Gross profit	$ 8,069	$ 5,306	$ 15,681	$ 12,349
Less corporation taxes (31.8%)	2,563	1,687	4,981	3,927
Net profit	$ 5,506	$ 3,619 (34.3% less)	$ 10,700	$ 8,422 (21.3% less)
Rate of return on net worth	8.71%	5.72%	14.31%	11.27%

*Gross revenue
**Decreased by the same percentage as landings quantities (i.e., 10%)
[1] **Source:** For columns headed **Data from Source** is table 4, page 9 of the **New England Business Review,** August, 1965.

If, by fortuitous circumstance or good management, landings of haddock were to increase by 10 percent per month, *ceteris paribus,* gross revenue, net profit, and the rate of return on net worth would *rise* by proportions equal to those just described. Details of these computations are in Table 2.

TABLE 2

**EFFECTS ON GROSS REVENUE OF A 10% INCREASE IN
NEW ENGLAND HADDOCK LANDINGS,
BASED ON DATA FOR 1963-64** [1]

	Conventional Side Trawler		Stern Trawler	
	Data from Source	With 5.4% increase in G. R.	Data from Source	With 5.4% increase in G.R.
Investment				
Equity in first year	$ 63,230	No change	$ 74,750	No change
Revenue				
Value of catch (28 trips)*	$160,000	$168,640	$192,000	$202,368
Less shared cost of operation	9,658	10,624**	11,130	12,243**
Net revenue	$150,342	$158,016	$180,870	$190,125
Less crew share (64% of N.R.)	96,219	101,130	115,757	121,680
Vessel share	$ 54,123	$ 56,886	$ 65,113	$ 68,445
Fixed expenses	46,054	No change	49,432	No change
Gross profit	$ 8,069	$ 10,832	$ 15,681	$ 19,013
Less corporation taxes (31.8%)	2,563	3,445	4,981	6,046
Net profit	$ 5,506	$ 7,387 (34.2% more)	$ 10,700	$ 12,967 (21.2% more)
Rate of return on net worth	8.71%	11.68%	14.31%	17.35%

*Gross revenue.
**Increased by the same percentage as landings quantities (i.e., 10%)
[1] Source: For columns headed **Data from Source** is table 4, page 9 of the **New England Business Review**, August, 1965.

The effects of a change in demand for haddock due to changes in the region's catch of other species of fish can also be important. With an upward change of 10% in the weighted average price of "all fish" (as defined before), a 3.8% increase in gross revenue in the haddock fishery would result. Assuming the opposite situation, a 10% reduction of the "all fish" price, however, would lead to a slightly greater reduction in gross revenue over the period (4.1%). In terms of gross revenue over the years 1963-64, this would have meant an increase of $889,241 in gross revenue from haddock, given the upward movement in the "all fish" price, but a loss of $953,782 in haddock revenues given the opposite situation.

There are sharp increases in New England haddock landings during the March through June period. One may postulate increases in production due to optimum conditions in the fleet (a good labor climate, maximum vessel availability) and unusually good weather during this period. On the other hand, as has occurred in the past, labor troubles and sustained inclement weather conditions may drastically reduce the catch during the peak period.

If, during the peak period, landings were increased by 10%, or decreased by a similar proportion, one may assume *a priori* that proportional changes in gross revenue during the period considered would be about the same as in the first case discussed. However, since the 10% change was applied only to part of the year, the result was a 2.1% change in total gross revenue from haddock over the two-year period in either direction, as appropriate, or approximately half of the variation resulting from the across-the-board increases or decreases discussed in the first case.

If one postulates the existence of conditions in other fisheries similar to those postulated for the haddock fishery, effects on haddock revenues are not as great. A 10% change in the quantities of "other" fish landed, given stability in haddock landings, produced a 1.5% change in gross revenue from haddock in the opposite direction.

Seasonal Considerations

Well defined indications of a major increase in consumption of fish in the early part of the calendar year corresponding to the observance of Lent have been found. These effects have been noted primarily in landings and wholesale prices, movements from storage, and in family expenditure studies.

Although the results in general were somewhat clouded by the weakness of the system in the middle-market area, the model produced several parameters which corroborate the presence of a shift in the haddock market.

Two dramatic examples of an apparent Lenten demand shift may be presented from geographically quite divergent areas. The examples also reflect different commodity bases since one refers to fish in Boston and the other to all seafood in Michigan.

Figure 2 shows the relationship of the average monthly landings and associated prices paid to fishermen for all food fish in Boston, 1958-62. With some reservations (primarily concerning the effect of other variables which are omitted), one may explain the two levels in the figure, traced out by the free-hand lines D-D and D′-D′, as representative of this annual demand shift. Granting seasonal supply shifts, the shifting supply curves seem to trace out two definite levels of demand.

Figure 3 shows the expenditures for fish and seafood, by four-week periods, averaged for the years 1954-58, by the Michigan State University consumer panel, a group of 275 families selected to be representative of the population of Lansing, Michigan. The sharp peaking of expenditures occurs approximately during Lent.

Seasonal effects were estimated using the two, half-year, landings demand equations. These were as follows:

Jan.-June: $Y_1^a = 2.8727 - .450848Z_1 + .866876Z_9 + .345814Y_3$

July-Dec.: $Y_1 = 4.3839 - .565570Z_1 + .746855Z_9 + .183672Y_3^b$

[a] Symbols defined earlier.
[b] Not significantly different from zero at the 5 per cent level.

Assuming that there is little change or no change from one season to another, and that the relationships during the entire year are those prevailing in the July-December period (when elasticities are lower), revenue, it was found, would have declined to approximately 93% of its actual average value in 1963, and to 82% of its value in 1964. The demand shift in the January-June period, then, would have an approximate value of 17-18% of gross revenues. That is to say, if the conditions of 1963 with respect to landings prevailed, but there were no shifts in demand during the January-June period from the July-December period, revenues would have been 17-18% lower than the revenue before the demand shift took place.

Consider the implications then of an amelioration of this shift that might arise were dietary restraints during Lent reduced in importance. It is possible that this underestimates the importance of the shift since a substantial proportion of the sales in the winter period come from stocks accumulated earlier. This tends to mitigate the shift as it has been measured here.

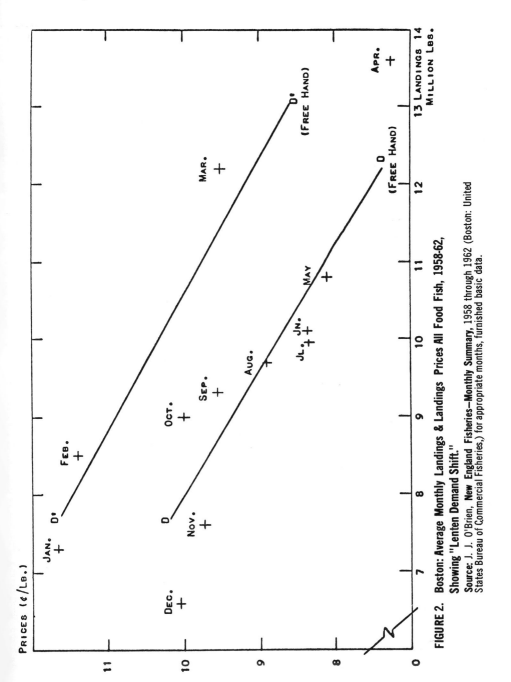

FIGURE 2.   Boston: Average Monthly Landings & Landings Prices All Food Fish, 1958-62, Showing "Lenten Demand Shift."

Source: J. J. O'Brien, **New England Fisheries—Monthly Summary,** 1958 through 1962 (Boston: United States Bureau of Commercial Fisheries,) for appropriate months, furnished basic data.

Demand for Fish Products

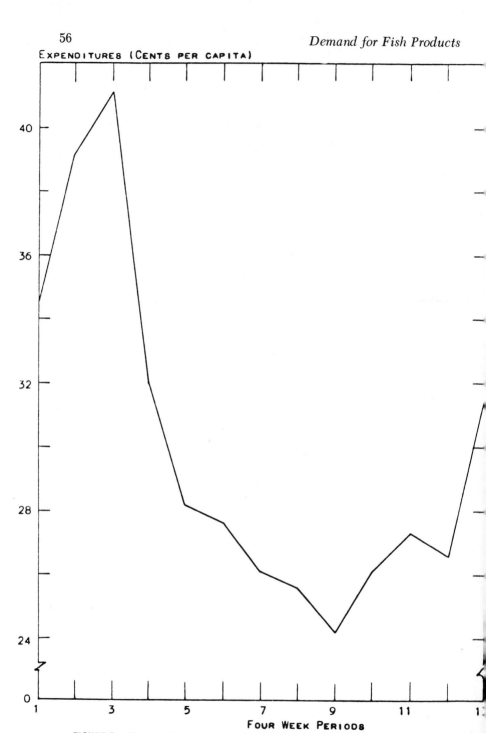

FIGURE 3. Michigan State University Sample: Expenditures for fish and sea food; seasonal averages, 1954-58.

There are several possible approaches to speculating about the impact of a shift none of which is unassailable. The estimates just given are rather impressive in magnitude.

It is also possible to assess seasonal influences by evaluating the difference between revenues under an assumed year-round stability at July-December levels, and the all-year average levels. When this was done, it was found that revenues were reduced to about 93 percent of the 1963-64 levels.

Another approach is to consider the demand curves for the seasons to be appropriate, and the average period (whole year, in the equations) to represent a "no seasonal difference" condition. The shift measured in this way is reflected in 89% and 88% achievement of the 1963 and 1964 revenue levels, respectively. Thus it appears safe to say that were seasonal patterns of demand to be eliminated, revenues would decline, and by some proportion varying from 7% to 17%.

Summary and Conclusions

Certain equations of a model of the markets for haddock in New England were tested for reliability. These tests indicate that the parameters developed are reliable enough to gauge the effects of changes in several variables on gross revenue obtained from haddock in New England fishing ports.

Five hypothetical situations were posed and their effects on gross revenue from haddock were measured. First, the effects of changes in the landings quantity of haddock were examined. Ten percent changes each month led to about 5.4% changes in the value of the catch in the same direction. Using a recent study as a guide, it was found that this might be reflected quite drastically in net profit and returns on net worth to the average boat.

Next the effects were studied of an across-the-board increase of 10% in the composite price of all finned food fish, reflecting perhaps an upward shift in consumer demand for these species. It was found that these changes would raise gross revenue from haddock about 4%. In the opposite situation, the decrease would be of about the same magnitude.

Adding to, or reducing, the volume of the catch of haddock during peak months of March through June, with stability through the rest of the year, changed gross revenue for the year by about 2% in the same direction as the quantity change. On the other hand, changing the volume of other fish landed by 10% either way led to only a 1.5% change in revenues from haddock, in the same direction.

By far the most significant hypothesis was concerned with the effect on gross revenues from haddock if the high late winter and early spring (Lenten) demands no longer existed. In this eventuality, it was found that revenues from haddock would decline from 7% to 17% depending on the degree of severity of the assumed conditions. Assuming that eating fish on Fridays and during Lent is not a deeply ingrained regional habit, the removal of restrictions of a religious nature may have drastic effects on revenues.

Another major conclusion one may draw from these studies is that planned improvements in the fleet which could lead to increases in quantities landed would also increase gross revenue. However, the gross revenue would increase proportionally less than the increase in catches.

APPENDIX I

PARAMETERS OF THE HADDOCK MODEL
(in natural logarithms)

Whole year results

Landings:

S: $Z_L = C$ (E1)

D: $Y_1 = 2.8727 - .450448Z_1 + .773113Z_9 + .390029Y_3$ (E2)

D: $Y_3 = 4.9798 + .397090Y_1 - .316785Z_4 - .072375Z_3$ (E3)

Wholesale:

S: $Y_6 = 12.1610 - 1.31821Y_8 + .84022Z_9 - .08094Z_3^a$ (E4)

D: $Y_6 = 14.5166 + 1.40144Z_9 - 1.11151Y_8 - 1.49905Y_7$ (E5)

Imports:

S: $Y_4 = 1.3754 - .15799Z_9^a + .86368Z_5 - .02652Z_2^a$ (E6)

D: $Y_4 = 9.4973^a - .35115Z_9^a - 1.43815Z_{10}^a - .01713Z_2^a$ (E7)

Cold Storage:

S: $Y_9 = 25.5449 + 3.39820Y_1^a - .12464Y_4^a - 5.88317Y_8$
$\qquad - .10452Z_1^a + .06823Z_2$ (E8)

D: $Y_9 = 10.0266 - 1.05887Y_{10}^a - 51.70506Y_{12}$
$\qquad + 5.10717Z_{10} - .04703Z_2$ (E9)

Retail:

S: $Y_7 = 10.5336 - .55473Y_6 + .00997Z_9^a - .12374Z_3$ (E10)

D: $Y_7 = -1.4340 + .03100Y_6^a + .82598Z_7 + .22331Z_8$ (E11)

January through June

Landings:

S: $Z_L = C$ (E1)

D: $Y_1 = 2:8727 - .450848Z_1 + .866876Z_9 + .345814Y_3$ (E2)

D: $Y_3 = 4.6537 + .456850Y_1 - .306042Z_4 - .063328Z_3$ (E3)

Wholesale:

S: $Y_6 = 8.6379 - 1.15308Y_8 + .99565Z_9^a + .14936Z_3^a$ (E4)

D: $Y_6 = 14.7189 + .73657Z_9 - .48361Y_8 - 1.50988Y_7$ (E5)

Imports:

S: $Y_4 = 2.7362 + .00354Z_9^a + .64616Z_5 - .01120Z_2^a$ (E6)

D: $Y_4 = 8.4100^a + .01920Z_9^a - .22579Z_{10}^a - .00918Z_2^a$ (E7)

Cold Storage:

S: $Y_9 = 31.7287 + 3.27744Y_1^a - .21782Y_4^a - .40947Y_8$
$\qquad - .40013Z_1^a - .12638Z_2^a$ (E8)

D: $Y_9 = 9.7106 - .03575Y_{10}^a - 44.00343Y_{12}$
$\qquad + 4.29533Z_{10} - .01777Z_2^a$ (E9)

Retail:

S: $Y_7 = 10.6317 - .63241Y_6 + .05189Z_9^a - .07478Z_3^a$ (E10)

D: $Y_7 = -4.4800 + .20326Y_6 + 1.03225Z_7 + .30219Z_8$ (E11)

July through December

Landings:

  S: $Z_L = C$ (E1)

  D: $Y_1 = 4.3839 - .565570Z_1 + .746855Z_9 + .183672Y_3^a$ (E2)

  D: $Y_3 = 3.6698 + .339413Y_1 - .265183Z_4 + .009190Z_3^a$ (E3)

Wholesale:

  S: $Y_6 = 10.1934 - 1.39554Y_8 + .92512Z_9^a + .08670Z_3^a$ (E4)

  D: $Y_6 = 14.1426 + 1.14340Z_9 - 1.07646Y_8 - 1.23235Y_7$ (E5)

Imports:

  S: $Y_4 = 2.6730 - .31365Z_9^a + .77350Z_5 - .04323Z_2^a$ (E6)

  D: $Y_4 = 11.7082 - 1.00808Z_9^a + 1.36395Z_{10}^a - .05352Z_2$ (E7)

Cold Storage:

  S: $Y_9 = 9.9019 + 1.44854Y_1^a - .11143Y_4^a - 2.01086Y_8^a$

             $+ .56740Z_1^a - .06649Z_2$ (E8)

  D: $Y_9 = 10.3531 - 3.34294Y_{10} - 3.76387Y_{12}^a$

             $+ 5.05281Z_{10}^a - .07857Z_2$ (E9)

Retail:

  S: $Y_7 = 6.0013 - .42025Y_6 + .15938Z_9^a + .11837Z_3^a$ (E10)

  D: $Y_7 = 2.7788 - .22683Y_6 + .67164Z_7 + .03728Z_3^a$ (E11)

[a] Not significantly different from zero at the 5 per cent level.

LIST OF SYMBOLS USED IN THE EQUATIONS

Mutually dependent endogenous	Variables = Predetermined or exogenous
Y_1 = Landings price	Z_1 = Landings quantities
Y_2 = Not used	Z_2 = Cold storage holdings (t-1)
Y_3 = Landings price, "all fish"	Z_3 = Cold storage holdings, "other fish"
Y_4 = Imports quantities	Z_4 = Landings quantities, "other fish"
Y_5 = Not used	Z_5 = Landings quantities, Canada
Y_6 = Net market movement	Z_6 = Not used
Y_7 = Consumer price, frozen fillets	Z_7 = Consumer price index, all meats
Y_8 = Wholesale price, fresh fillets	Z_8 = Personal income
Y_9 = Cold storage holdings	Z_9 = Wholesale price, frozen fillets
Y_{10} = Not used	Z_{10} = Changes in WP frozen fillets
Y_{11} = Changes in WP fresh fillets	
Y_{12} = Changes in CP frozen fillets	

Other Conventional Symbols

Z_L = Landings quantities, any and all fish   S: = Supply   D: = Demand

COMMENT

VINCENT F. DUNFEY

Boston College

Once upon a time, before the dawn of the computer age, I ground out some multiple regressions on a calculator and called it a study of the demand for haddock in the New England area.[1] This is why I am here to discuss the application of Farrell and Lampe's imposing ten-equation model of the haddock market.

While the advent of the computer has eased computional difficulties, I note that informational difficulties persist. There still are not sufficient statistics and statistics of the right type to satisfactorily test the model. Hopefully, conferences of this type will contribute to the solution of this problem.

I would like first to discuss the model from which Farrell and Lampe's estimates of returns to boat owners were made. The main objective of the model was "to provide meaningful estimates of the demand for the haddock products of the New England fishing industry at the various levels between the fishermen and the national consumers." I suggest that most of the haddock landed in New England does not reach the national market; that there are, in fact, two markets, one for fresh haddock and the other for frozen haddock and haddock products; and that the first of these markets is primarily local, and the other national.

How much of the haddock landed in New England goes into the fresh market, and how much is frozen? The available information on distribution is sketchy although the next paper to be given may very well supply some definitive answers. On the basis of data from the Packaged Fish reports of the Bureau of Commercial Fisheries I estimate that approximately two-thirds of the haddock landed in New England is sold fresh and one-third is frozen.

Whatever the exact proportions there are two distinct markets from which the demand of wholesaler-processors for haddock is derived. The fresh market consists of restaurants and food stores in the New England and New York area. The frozen market is nationwide.

---

[1] Vincent F. Dunfey, *A Study of the Economic Factors Affecting the Demand for New England Cod and Haddock*, (Bureau of Business Research, College of Business Administration, Boston College, August, 1961).

The fresh market feels little competition from foreign suppliers while the frozen market is supplied principally by imports. Fresh haddock retail prices vary with the season of the year. Frozen haddock fillet retail prices, as reported from some 40 cities by the Bureau of Labor Statistics, show no seasonal variation.

The demand for haddock for the fresh market seems to be less elastic (price is more sensitive to increases or decreases in landings) than for the frozen market. This is perhaps because there are consumers and restaurant patrons who will continue to eat haddock despite changes in price. Above a certain reservation price it is uneconomic to buy haddock for the frozen market. Below this price the demand for haddock to freeze is probably quite elastic (relatively little change in price as landings increase or decrease).

In the landings market these types of demand join, forming a kinked demand curve with the less elastic fresh demand dominating above the reservation price, and the more elastic frozen demand dominating below this price.

This hypothesis provides an alternative, or, at least, an additional explanation of the differences in elasticity found by Farrell and Lampe in the two periods (January-June and July-December) they used. The ultimate consumer of fresh haddock will pay more so the price is bid up in periods of low landings. When it rises above the reservation price, buying for freezing decreases, input to cold storage declines, and holdings drop, since the quantity sold is stable. As landings increase in the spring, the price decreases below the reservation price, buying for freezing increases, inputs increase and holdings rise.

Thus, I suggest that a satisfactory explanation of the demand for New England haddock in the landings market must include the relatively local factors which determine fresh haddock demand and the national and international factors which determine demand for frozen haddock from New England.

I do have some reservations concerning the conclusions of the paper. The predictions of returns to boat owners are based only on their landings equations. One of the variables determining haddock landings price is "all fish" landings price, which in turn is determined partially by the haddock landings price. Since haddock is the principal component of the "all fish" category the usefulness of the landings price equation would seem to be limited. Let me hasten to add that the authors must have used this variable for lack of satisfactory statistics for other competing products.

Finally, I would like to comment upon the effect of the removal of the Catholic restriction on meat-eating. How damaging this is to the New England groundfishing industry depends, obviously, on how many Catholics are buying fish because they may not eat meat, and how many buy because they like good fish. I suggest that those who are forced to buy are perhaps buying the frozen, prepared product, while those who like sea food are fresh haddock customers. Since the New England industry primarily serves the fresh haddock market the lifting of restrictions may not deal the industry the severe blow some have predicted.

THE MARKET FOR FRESH FISH THAT ORIGINATE FROM BOSTON FISH PIER LANDINGS*

*FREDERICK L. GASTON AND DAVID A. STOREY***

University of Massachusetts

There has been a scarcity of organized attempts to improve and expand markets for domestic commercial fishery products. One reason for this situation is the fact that many commercial fishery product markets are not well defined. To improve or expand the market for a product, it is necessary first to understand the extent and characteristics of the existing market.

This paper is a report of an attempt to improve the state of knowledge about one domestic fishery products market. The market investigated was that for fish landed at the Boston Fish Pier by the Boston trawler fleet. Boston is the leading U.S. port for landings of haddock, cod and pollock.

The objectives of the study reported here were to describe in what geographic areas the Boston fish are consumed, in what form they are consumed or retailed, and what market channels the fish flow through on their passage to the place of final consumption or retail sale. The four leading species in Boston—haddock, cod, pollock and flounder (including sole)—were studied individually and collectively. Three different months—August 1964, December 1964, and March 1965—were analyzed, to account for average, light and heavy landing months, and for seasonal demand variations.

*The research reported in this paper was financed by a grant from the Bureau of Commercial Fisheries, U.S. Department of the Interior.
**Research Assistant and Associate Professor in the Department of Agricultural and Food Economics, University of Massachusetts.

It should be made clear that this is only a preliminary report, and presents only highlights of the findings of the study. Some analyses of data are still in progress, and a more complete and detailed report will be published in the future.

As a starting point, it was known that nearly all the fish landed at the Boston Fish Pier are purchased at the auction in the New England Fish Exchange by a group of about 40 to 50 dealer-processors and by two large food chains which do their own processing. The dealer-processors are located on or near the Fish Pier. Fish leave the trawlers in round form, with the entrails removed. Dealer-processors sell some fish in the same form as received, some are scaled, some are sold in steaked form (head removed) and some are sold as fillets (head, fins, and bones removed, and sometimes the skin is removed). Since landings fluctuate seasonally, the surplus in months of heavy landings is frozen and put in cold storage to be sold later in months of lighter landings. The fresh or frozen fish is trucked to its place of final consumption or retail sale, in some instances passing through intermediary dealers or processors before reaching the end of the marketing channel.

Procedure Used to Study the Market

The initial plan for tracing the movement of the fish was simple in concept. A representative sample of the Fish Pier dealer-processors was to be selected and each dealer was to be asked to provide information on sales of the four species during the three months under study. The information was to identify the quantity of each product form (whole, steaked or filleted) of each species sold, and the names of the recipients of each lot sold. Then, at each successive stage in the marketing channel, a sample of the firms involved was to be interviewed, until the fish had been traced to its final point of consumption or retail sales. From the set of successive samples, it would be possible to make inferences about the total market for Boston fish—where each species was consumed and in what form, and what types of marketing firms were involved in the processing and movement of the fish.

The original plan had to be discarded after the field work was started. The dealers on the Fish Pier were in many cases interested in the objectives of the study. However, in nearly all cases they refused to provide access to the detailed information sought, because they did not want to reveal their clienteles.

An alternative approach was tried next. The names of trucking firms that hauled fish from Fish Pier dealers were obtained. Twelve truckers agreed to provide information about shipments during the three months. The information identified the quantity of fish shipped from Fish Pier dealers to various recipients. In most instances it did not identify the species or product form.

The cooperating truckers were important haulers of fish from the Boston Fish Pier. Every known dealer in the Fish Pier area used at least one of the cooperating trucking firms during the three months studied. However, each trucking firm served a special geographical area. When a trucker refused to cooperate or could not be contacted, the area served by that trucker was not covered in the study, thus giving a geographical bias to the results. The apparent principal omissions of this type were Baltimore, Washington, D.C., Chicago, and Louisville, Kentucky. Shipments to points near Boston also were not covered by the trucker information, as most of the truckers served out-of-state destinations.

Over 400 firms identifed as recipients of Boston fish from the trucker information were visited and interviewed. The interviews determined the breakdown of each shipment by species and product form, the classification of the recipient's type of business, and the type of business to which the fish were resold, if it was not retailed or consumed in the recipient's premises. In addition, 313 mail questionnaires were sent to recipients that were not interviewed personally. One hundred of these questionnaires were completed and returned. Also, 295 mail questionnaires were sent to probable handlers of Boston fish for which no prior shipment information had been obtained. Sixty-two of these questionnaires were completed and returned.

Other sources of data were used also. The two food chain store firms in Boston that processed fish supplied information about Fish Pier purchases of the selected species for the three months. They also provided some limited information about geographic distribution. Four non-processing food chains in the Boston area also provided information about purchases of fish from Fish Pier dealers. Together, the six food chains accounted for 42 percent of New England grocery sales in 1964.[1] Three of the six sold products outside New England also.

---

[1] Based on data in the *Yankee Grocer*. March 8, 1965.

The Government purchasing agency in Boston supplied information about purchases of fish from the Fish Pier and about geographical distribution of the fish. The purchases were entirely of frozen products and were required to be of domestic origin.

The major cold storage facility used by the Fish Pier dealers offered to provide information. However, although quantities of out-movements were available and they were broken down by species, the recipient was seldom identified on the orders. Therefore, the data had limited usefulness.

After a year spent collecting data, a second attempt was made to gather information from the primary Fish Pier dealers. This time the researchers were better informed about the distributive practices of the Boston dealers. Armed with this knowledge, they were relatively more successful, as four of the 23 firms contacted agreed to permit collection of data from their records. Product sales were obtained for the three months, and they were broken down by species, product form and classification of recipient's type of business. Follow-up interviews with recipients were not made, because the study was nearly completed at that time. Six other Fish Pier dealers offered some estimates of distributive activities that were helpful in giving general perspective, but were not complete or detailed enough to be included in the principal tabulations.

The original intent of the study was to describe both the fresh and frozen fish market for the four principal species landed in Boston. As stated earlier, the dealers may sell fish immediately as fresh fish, or they may freeze it, put it in cold storage, and sell it later as frozen fish. However, Fish Pier dealers prefer to sell domestic fish as fresh fish, because frozen fish may be obtained more cheaply from foreign sources. Many Boston dealers purchased imported frozen fish, and some had the reputation of dealing almost exclusively in foreign fish. Where information was obtained from sources other than the originating dealers, such as from the trucking firms, it was impossible to determine whether frozen fish was of domestic or foreign origin. As the study progressed, it became apparent that the domestic and foreign frozen fish markets were intermixed, but foreign frozen fish were the dominant factor. Therefore the emphasis of the study was put on a description of the fresh fish market.

At this point, it may be useful to pause and summarize the sources of data for the market description that will follow. Information about fresh fish marketings was collected from five major types of sources: (1) twelve trucking firms that hauled fish from Boston Fish Pier dealers to various destinations, (2) about 500 inland wholesalers, retailers, restaurants, institutions and other recipients of the shipments identified from the trucking firm records, (3) 62 other probable handlers of Boston fish for which no prior shipment information had been obtained, (4) four Fish Pier dealer-processors, and (5) six food chain store firms located in Boston, two of which processed Boston fish. Where possible, the information from the different sources was combined, but in many instances each set of data had to be handled separately.

Description of the Market

The market description that will follow will cover only fish originating from Boston Fish Pier landings that were marketed as fresh fish. Only haddock, cod, pollock and flounder are included and the study covers only the three months of August 1964, December 1964, and March 1965.

Table 1 compares the total quantities of fresh fish marketings accounted for in the study tabulations to the total quantities of fish landed at the Fish Pier during the study months. All quantities are shown in round weight equivalents, to make the comparisons meaningful. After eliminating duplication of coverage among the different sources, 50 percent of the landings in the three months were accounted for by the marketing information collected in the study.

TABLE 1.

MARKETINGS OF FRESH HADDOCK, COD, POLLOCK AND FLOUNDER ACCOUNTED FOR IN THE STUDY, COMPARED TO BOSTON FISH PIER LANDINGS

Source of information	August 1964	December 1964	March 1965	Three months combined
(thousand pounds of fish—round weight equivalent)				
Truckers	1,926	1,460	2,693	6,079
Fish Pier dealers	982	899	1,582	3,462
Other handlers	216	271	371	858
Boston food chains	697	587	1,148	2,431
All sources combined [a]	3,621	3,069	5,528	12,218
Fish Pier landings [b]	8,496	5,377	10,421	24,294
Percent of landings accounted for	43	57	53	50

[a] Smaller than sum of column above, because duplicate coverage was eliminated.
[b] **Source:** John J. O'Brien, **New England Fisheries—Monthly Summary,** August 1964, December 1964 and March 1965, U.S. Department of the Interior, Bureau of Commercial Fisheries, Market News Service, Boston, Massachusetts.

Only a rough approximation of the coverage of the study is given in Table 1. Even if all fish landed were marketed as fresh fish, marketings for a month would not coincide with landings, because of the lag between the time the fish is landed and the time it is sold. In addition, some fish is frozen and sold as frozen fish. In the case of frozen fish, there is no correlation in a given month between landings volume and sales volume. What is not known, of course, is how much of the difference between landings and the marketings accounted for in the study is attributable to sales of fresh fish that were not accounted for and how much is attributable to fish that were frozen and sold at a later date.

Geographic Distribution

The first question to be answered is in what geographic areas were the fish consumed? Each of the four sources of information had a different geographic emphasis, as indicated in Table 2. When the data were combined, and duplication was eliminated, the aggregate geographic distribution of the fish accounted for in the study appeared as shown in Figure 1.

Somewhat less than one-half of the fresh fish shipments identified stayed in New England, with most of those fish being consumed in Massachusetts. Nearly one-third of the fish marketings accounted for occurred in the State of New York. The western half of New York was a particularly important market, as 16 percent of the total fish marketings occurred in the area around the three cities of Syracuse, Rochester and Buffalo. New York, Pennsylvania and Ohio combined accounted for slightly over one-half of the fresh fish sales identified. Small amounts of fish were traced as far away as Texas, Minnesota and Florida.

Even though half of the fish landings for the three months were accounted for in the study, the samples were not necessarily representative, so the results cannot simply be multiplied by two to describe the total geographic market. Nearly half of the basic information was collected from the truckers, and 93 percent of the truck shipments identified went to New York, Pennsylvania and Ohio. Markets in those states were probably covered very thoroughly. Other out-of-state markets such as Baltimore, Washington, D.C., Chicago, and Louisville, Kentucky were covered much less completely. Of even more importance, local markets in New England were not covered thoroughly. Most of the New England information

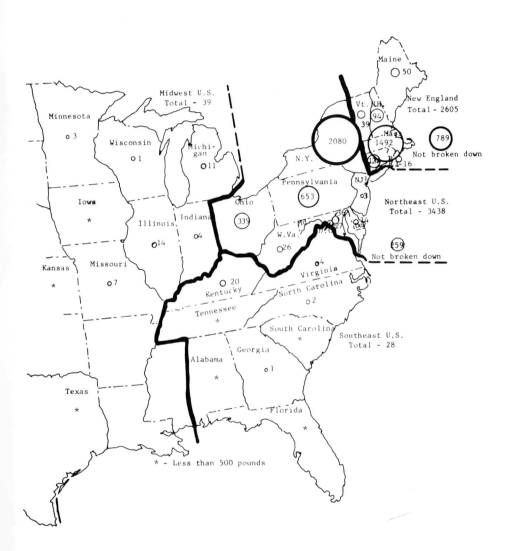

FIGURE 1. Thousand Pounds of Fresh Fish Identified in the Study That Were Shipped to Different States and Areas

TABLE 2

RECEIPTS OF FRESH HADDOCK, COD, POLLOCK AND FLOUNDER
BY GEOGRAPHIC AREA AND SOURCE OF INFORMATION
(August 1964, December 1964 and March 1965 Combined)

Geographic area	Source of Information				
	Truckers	Fish Pier dealers	Other handlers	Boston food chains	All sources combined [a]
	(thousand pounds of fish in shipment weights)				
New England					
Mass.	42	920	373	203	1,492
Other	101	271	–	789	1,113
Total	143	1,191	373	992	2,605
North East					
New York	1,847	413	–	–	2,080
Ohio	229	16	99	–	340
Penn.	434	131	132	–	652
Other	36	75	8	259	336
Total	2,546	635	239	259	3,438
South East	–	28	–	–	28
Mid West	–	39	–	–	39
Grand Total	2,689	1,893	612	1,251	6,110

[a] Smaller than sum of line because duplicate coverage eliminated.

originated from the four cooperating Fish Pier dealers, the six large food chains and the 31 fish handlers in Massachusetts that returned mail questionnaires. Many potential handlers in New England were not contacted.

However, a large enough portion of landings was accounted for to permit some rough estimates of the total geographic market. Assuming that somewhere between 70 and 90 percent of landings in the three months were sold as fresh fish, probably 50 to 60 percent of total fresh fish sales were made in New England, 30 to 40 percent in New York, Pennsylvania and Ohio and 5 to 15 percent in other out-of-state markets.

The Form in Which Products Were Marketed

Were fish shipped in whole, steaked or filleted form? The importance of different product forms varied among species. The filleted form was most important for haddock, but more flounder were shipped whole than filleted (Figure 2). Cod and pollock were most often sold steaked or filleted, with steaks relatively more important for cod, and fillets for pollock.

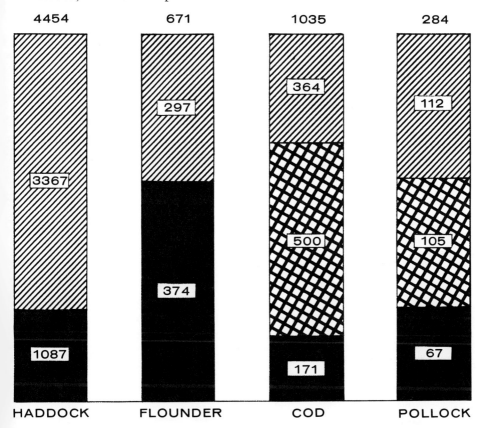

FIGURE 2. Relative Importance of Different Product Forms for the Four Species, in Thousands of Pounds Shipped.

Note: The above totals include some duplication (about 5 percent), because it was not possible to break down duplicate coverage by individual species.

 Fillets Steak Whole

Geographical Differences in Species and Product Form

Shipments of each species to each of the four major regions are shown in Table 3. These aggregate data do not reveal striking differences in geographic markets for the four species, as similar proportions were shipped to each region. A possible exception is cod, which appeared to be consumed in greater proportion outside New England, compared to the other three species. Over one-third of the

TABLE 3

**RELATIVE IMPORTANCE OF DIFFERENT PRODUCT
FORMS IN THE FOUR CHIEF GEOGRAPHIC AREAS**
(August 1964, December 1964, and March 1965 Combined)

Species and Product Form	Geographic Area				
	New England	North East	South East	Mid West	All areas combined
	(thousand pounds of fish in shipment weights)[a]				
Haddock					
Fillets	888	2,436	21	21	3,367
Whole	1,055	31	–	1	1,087
Total	1,943	2,467	21	22	4,454
Cod					
Fillets	95	267	*	2	364
Steak	168	329	2	1	500
Whole	88	84	–	*	172
Total	351	680	2	3	1035
Pollock					
Fillets	41	71	1	*	113
Steak	36	69	–	–	105
Whole	51	16	–	–	67
Total	128	156	1	*	284
Flounder					
Fillets	156	127	3	10	296
Whole	121	249	1	3	374
Total	277	376	4	13	671

[a] Data include some duplication (above five percent) because it was not possible to separate duplicate coverage by individual species.
* Less than 500 pounds.

cod accounted for was marketed in New York. New York City appeared to be a particularly important cod market. Pennsylvania also appeared to be an important cod market. Although pollock was not consumed outside New England in greater proportion than were haddock or flounder, marketings of pollock were concentrated in southeastern New York, eastern Pennsylvania, Maryland and West Virginia. On the other hand, nearly all the fish marketings identified in Ohio were of haddock.

The forms in which products were shipped varied considerably among regions (Table 3). Over half of the haddock marketed in New England was sold as whole fish, while nearly all the haddock marketed outside New England was sold as fillets. A different situation existed for flounder, for sales in filleted form were relatively more important in New England, and sales in whole form were relatively more important outside New England.

TABLE 4

CLASSIFICATION OF INITIAL RECIPIENTS OF FISH, BY SOURCE OF INFORMATION
(August 1964, December 1964, and March 1965 Combined)

Initial recipient classification	Sources of Information				
	Truckers	Fish Pier dealers	Other handlers	Boston food chains	All sources combined [a]
	(thousand pounds of fish in shipment weights)				
Retailers	177	1,197	314	1,251	2,911
Wholesaler-Retailers	1,148	43	65	—	1,136
Wholesalers	851	188	212	—	1,238
Restaurants	171	289	14	—	396
Specialty outlets	185	93	4	—	208
Institutions	44	83	2	—	117
Unclassified	113	—	—	—	104 [b]
All types combined	2,689	1,893	611	1,251	6,110

[a] Smaller than sum of line, because duplicate coverage was eliminated.
[b] Nine thousand pounds duplicated in the information from truckers and dealers were unclassified in the trucker data, and therefore, were subtracted from this trucker classification, although they appear in some other classification in the dealer column.

Types of Firms That Handled the Fish

A breakdown of initial recipients of the fish by type of firm is shown in Table 4. It should be noted that the relative importance of different classifications varied among the sources of information. Overall, about 40 percent of the fish was handled by some type of intermediate wholesaler, while most of the remainder went directly to the final recipients. In the case of the food chains, some intermediate handling was involved also.

As would be expected, wholesalers and wholesaler-retailers were more important outside New England than in the nearby markets (Table 5). Sixty-six percent of the fish in the Northeast region was handled by wholesalers or wholesaler-retailers, compared to 6 percent in New England. In part, this was due to the fact that retailers provided directly much of the information about New England marketings. Intermediate wholesalers that were not identified may have handled more of the New England fish. However, it is logical to expect that wholesalers would be relatively unimportant in nearby markets.

TABLE 5

RELATIVE IMPORTANCE OF DIFFERENT INITIAL RECIPIENT CLASSIFICATIONS IN THE FOUR MAJOR REGIONS

(August 1964, December 1964, and March 1965 Combined)

Recipient classification	Geographic Region				
	New England	North East	South East	Mid West	All regions combined
	(percent of receipts in region) [a]				
Institutions	2	2	7	12	2
Wholesaler-Retailers	4	31	–	–	19
Wholesalers	2	35	11	1	21
Retailers	88	18	7	33	48
Restaurants	4	8	75	54	7
Specialty outlets	*	6	–	–	3
All classes combined	100	100	100	100	100

[a] Based on shipment weights, with duplication removed.
* Less than 0.5 percent.

The wholesalers and wholesaler-retailers that received shipments from the trucking firms were asked in interviews or by mail questionnaire to estimate the breakdown of their sales to different types of final recipients. The wholesaler-retailers retailed 36 percent of the fish they handled, and of their wholesale sales, 36 percent went to other retailers, 50 percent to restaurants and 14 percent to institutions. The wholesalers sold 61 percent of their fish to retailers, 33 percent to restaurants and 6 percent to institutions.

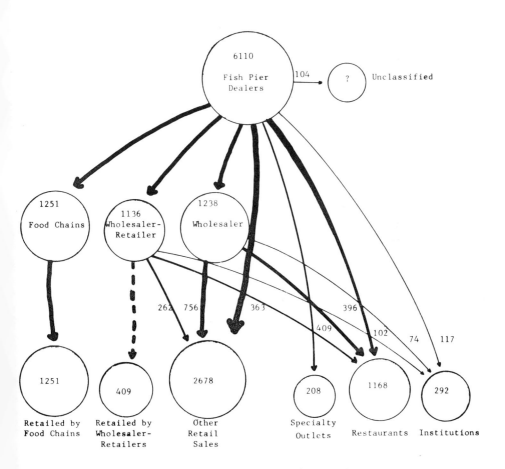

FIGURE 3. Composite Marketing Channels for Fresh Fish (Thousand Pounds Shipped)

The proportions indicated by the firms interviewed were applied to all sales by wholesalers and wholesaler-retailers to roughly approximate the composite of marketing channels (Figure 3).[2] Judging by the estimates presented in Figure 3 about 72 percent of the fish was sold to consumers in retail establishments, 19 percent in restaurants, 5 percent in institutions and 4 percent in specialty outlets (cooked fish sold to eat off the premises).

It was possible to divide sales between retail grocery stores and retail seafood markets for only about half of the total 4.3 million pounds sold in retail establishments. Of the 2.1 million pounds for which a breakdown was possible, 61 percent was sold in retail grocery stores and 39 percent was sold in retail seafood markets. The remaining 2.2 million pounds included sales to retailers by wholesalers and wholesaler-retailers, and direct sales to retailers by the four Boston Fish Pier dealers.

The data indicate that the restaurant and institutional market was somewhat more important for these species of fish than for all food in general. Overall, it has been estimated that eating places handle 17 percent of the U.S. food supply, while 24 percent of the Boston fish was handled by restaurants and institutions.[3]

Considerable amounts of fish were sold fried to eat off the premises. Specialty outlets that handled about 4 percent of the total fish specialized in this type of business. The retail seafood markets interviewed indicated that over half of their aggregate sales of the species studied were in fried form. Wholesalers did some of the cooking for the retail outlets they served, as about 16 percent of their sales to retail outlets were fried fish. Considering both retailers and specialty outlets, probably about one-fifth of the Boston fish marketed was sold as fried fish to eat off the premises. When these sales are added to sales by restaurants and institutions, it appears that nearly one-half of the Boston fish were cooked before being sold to consumers.

---

[2] To make the estimates presented in Figure 3 it was necessary to assume that all wholesalers and wholesaler-retailers had the same sales breakdown as the firms interviewed. The firms interviewed were located chiefly in New York, Pennsylvania and Ohio. If there are regional differences in sales patterns, the assumption might not be correct.

[3] Marguerite Burk, *Trends and Patterns in U.S. Food Consumption,* Agriculture Handbook No. 214, U.S. Department of Agriculture, Economic Research Service, June 1961, p. 79.

Seasonal Differences in Sales

If the marketing data collected in the study were representative, there were considerable seasonal variations in the marketing of fresh fish from Boston. Marketings of fresh fish were heaviest in March, the month of heaviest landings, and lightest in December, the month of lightest landings (Figure 4). Of course, the Lenten season occurred in March, making demand particularly strong in that month.

Marketings of haddock and pollock conformed closely to the aggregate seasonal variations. A particularly large percentage of cod landings was marketed in December, when landings were much lower than in the other two months. Nearly all the flounder landings were accounted for by the marketing data. There was no apparent reason why coverage of flounder landings should have been higher than for the other species. Therefore, it appears that the Boston dealers handled some flounder that was landed at other ports.

Conclusion

The data reported here give a rough picture of the market for haddock, cod, pollock, and flounder that were landed in Boston and were sold as fresh fish. The study was not as definitive as the authors had hoped originally, because it was not possible to draw representative samples. Some elements of the market were covered more thoroughly in the study than others, and the resulting composite picture may have been somewhat distorted.

Nevertheless, the study did account for about half of the fish landed at Boston during the three months, and therefore it did identify the major segments of the market, even if their relative importances were not described perfectly. Hopefully, the results of the study will be useful to those people concerned with this industry.

The market description does not answer questions about how to improve or develop the fresh fish market for haddock, cod, pollock or flounder landed at the Boston Fish Pier. It does, however, provide a framework within which meaningful questions may be asked.

Current newspaper reports have indicated that a forthcoming Papal bull will remove restrictions on Roman Catholic consumption of meat. The fisheries industry has depended heavily on the Roman Catholic market. This new development may change drastically the

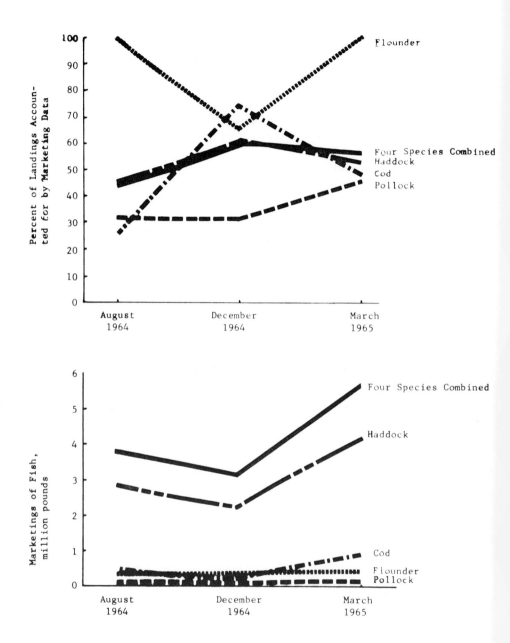

FIGURE 4. Marketings of Fish Accounted for in the Three Months, Total Quantities and Percentage of Landings (All Based on Round Weight Equivalents).

structure of the fish markets described here. It certainly will become even more important for those in the industry to focus attention on where and how they sell their fish.

As mentioned before, this was a preliminary report. Further analyses may clarify the description. More detailed information will be made available to those who wish to use it. If this study inspires more analytical studies of the important aspects of the market in question, or well-designed studies of other markets, it will have served an important purpose.

COMMENT

HUGH F. O'ROURKE

Boston Fisheries Association

The report, "The Market for Fresh Fish That Originate from Boston Fish Pier Landings," provided a comprehensive marketing analysis concerned with fish distribution. Undoubtedly, considerable investigation and patience was involved in acquiring knowledge of the distribution of fish that could be used on a definitive basis.

Although this report is related to the Boston Fish Pier, it would be advisable to include some reference to the United States and New England commercial fishing industry. The United States commercial fishing enterprise has been described as a fragmented industry—a business of many facets employing thousands of people from the local fisherman with his small boat, to the giants of the industry each with his immediate responsibility to supply food from the sea for human and industrial consumption.

The New England fishing industry, which dates from the Pilgrim Fathers, markets fresh fish, fresh frozen fish, and fish blocks. Landings at the Boston Fish Pier during the past three years average between 103,000,000 and 115,000,000 pounds per year, based upon the benevolence of Mother Nature. There is an average of 60 fishing vessels in the fleet supplying the Boston Fish Pier.

Boston is considered the largest supplier of fresh fish in the United States operating in one physical location. The report indicated that the market for Boston Fish is contained within a radius of 600 miles. Therefore, some may assume that beyond that distance it is difficult to transport fresh fish in good condition without freezing. With the progress being made in the field of refrigeration and with adequate supply of product, the fresh fish market can be expanded as far as the west coast. Studies relating to population growth have indicated that there are tremendous markets in the Midwest and Far West that offer great potential for New England fishery products.

It is interesting to note that 50 percent of the fish shipped from the Boston Fish Pier remains in New England and approximately 40 percent goes to markets in New York, Pennsylvania, and Ohio, with the remaining 10 percent transported South. This substantiates the national marketing picture that although the per capita consumption of fish is 10.6 pounds nationwide, yet it is approximately 30 pounds per capita in New England. It is the opinion of market analysts that there would be an increase in fish consumption nationwide if efforts were made to acquaint the Midwest with the value of fish as a food in the daily diet, providing that sufficient product was available. A recent survey by airlines confirms that the west coast wants New England fish products and with air freight cost reduced, haddock can become a daily menu item on the west coast.

When today's competition is so keen in a relatively small market area, it is not difficult to realize that the processing companies on the Fish Pier who were contacted regarding customers' location evidenced reluctance to provide this information. The actual sale of fish is a day-to-day process, closely related to a price structure that has its origin in the daily sale of fish by auction. A protective atmosphere exists within each company, closely guarding their customers' listings to meet the competitive market in their day-to-day transactions.

As stated in the report, the handling and the transporting of fish from the Boston Fish Pier warrants modernization. The Pier, which was built 50 years ago, has difficulty in handling the loading and unloading by the huge trailer truck of today. Consideration is being given to better handling methods—such as a central receiving and shipping depot, time saving devices for transferring fish within the Pier, etc.—that should result in time and equipment savings which in turn could be applied by better use of trucking equipment for transporting of fish to new markets.

The recent ruling changing the law of abstinence for Catholics in the United States to permit them to partake of meat on Friday, was met with some concern by leaders in the fishing industry. Traditionally because of the large Catholic population in the United States, fish marketing practices are directed toward Friday—yet a quick review of national fish consumption shows that in the past three years fish and seafood become part of the daily menu. However, if fish consumption declines as a result of the change in the abstinence laws the fishing industry may have to embark upon a highly concentrated advertising campaign—alerting the consumer to the value of fish as a food. Another important factor should be the development of a new marketing approach, accenting the sale of fish products in greater volume on days of the week other than Friday.

In summary, the efforts of the staff of the Department of Agriculture and Food Products, University of Massachusetts, in preparing this report should be commended. Although the information offered did not meet their original expectations, it can be said that this report will provide the Boston Fish Pier processors with invaluable information that can be utilized in research of potential markets.

COSTS
AND THE
YIELD
ON
CAPITAL

THE RELATION OF THE PRODUCTION FUNCTION TO THE YIELD ON CAPITAL FOR THE FISHING INDUSTRY

FREDERICK W. BELL

The Federal Reserve Bank of Boston

Most information on the returns to capital in the fishing industry has been developed either by the Tariff Commission or individual studies.[1] Unfortunately, the previous research in this area suffers from two main limitations. First, the sample of firms used may be challenged as unrepresentative of the industry. Little attempt has been made to obtain a "representative" cross section of the fishing industry. Second, most of the data are highly aggregative and do not reveal which segments of the industry are experiencing the greatest financial difficulty. In addition, most studies have concentrated only on profits (and losses) as financial indicators. While losses are a sure indicator of financial problems, profits must be related to the magnitude of investment in the particular enterprise to judge relative financial success. This paper will attempt to deal with some of these limitations in deriving estimates of the yield on capital for the fishing industry. In addition, a production function for the fishing enterprise will be developed and related to the yield on capital for various segments of the industry.

---

[1]See U.S. Tariff Commission, Groundfish Fillets (1956) Report to the President on Escape Clause Investigation No. 47, 1956 (proceed); E. J. Lynch, R. M. Doherty, and G. P. Draheim, *The Groundfish Industries of New England and Canada,* (United States Fish and Wildlife Service, Circular 121, 1961).

The Fishing Vessel Universe and Sample

In 1964, 726 fishing vessels were operating in the New England area. A list of these vessels was obtained from the Gloucester Office of the Bureau of Commercial Fisheries. The list includes the following characteristics of fishing vessels: 1) gross tons; 2) length; 3) age; 4) horsepower; 5) crew; 6) gear; 7) state; 8) county. The universe of fishing vessels was then analyzed by computing the means, standard deviations and other statistical measures. To develop information on financial performance, the universe was then stratified by those characteristics which might appreciably influence earnings. The *size, age, type of fishing*, and *region* were thought to be possible determinants of earning capabilities. In the case of age and tons the groupings reported in Table 1 were established on the basis of the mean values.[2] That is, 0-59 tons represents all vessels below the mean (59) while 60-320 includes all vessels above the mean. The actual stratification was done on a very detailed basis. For example, the interval distribution used for age of vessels was 5 years. The purpose of the rather gross classification reported here is that the sample was limited to 101 vessels in which no group or subdivision could be less than 5 vessels, in order to prevent disclosure of financial information for individual operations. Thus, group aggregates became necessary. Table 1 shows the stratification of the universe according to the first three characteristics.

Next, a sample of fishing vessels was selected. The sample selected has approximately the same characteristics with respect to gross tons, age and type of fishing as the universe. The sample was selected on a random basis from the detailed strata discussed above. However, the random selection procedure was subject to two major limitations:

1) only data on corporations were available

2) the sample was restricted to Massachusetts.

Although the sample selected from fishing corporations operating in the state has approximately the same characteristics (except re-

---

[2] The mean value on gross tons is 67.3 and on age, 23.6 years. However, 60 tons was selected as the division between large and small since vessels under 60 tons are generally considered "small." In addition, vessels from 0-19 years were classified as young since they were built in the postwar period. Thus, we have not completely adhered to dividing the sample at the means. In fact, the division is closer to the median values. Finally, the correlation of vessel length, one measure of size, and gross tons is very high. The coefficient of linear correlation between length and gross tons is .776. Naval architects claim that gross tons increase by the cube of the length. Any consideration of size should take this factor into account.

TABLE 1

DISTRIBUTION OF NEW ENGLAND FISHING VESSLES

BY AGE, SIZE AND TYPE OF FISHING

	Groundfish		Scallops		Other Fishing		Total	Percent
	Number	Percent	Number	Percent	Number	Percent		
Universe Divisions								
I 0-19 (Years) 0-59 (Tons)	131	(18.1)	4	(.6)	39	(5.4)	174	24.0
II 20-80 (Years) 0-59 (Tons)	204	(28.1)	7	(.9)	51	(7.0)	262	36.0
III 0-19 (Years) 60-320 (Tons)	95	(13.1)	34	(4.7)	7	(.9)	136	18.7
IV 20-80 (Years) 60-320 (Tons)	113	(15.7)	33	(4.5)	8	(1.0)	154	21.3
Total	543	(74.8)	78	(10.7)	105	(14.5)	726	100
Sample Divisions								
I 0-19 (Years) 0-59 (Tons)	19	(18.8)	0	0	6	(5.9)	25	24.8
II 20-80 (Years) 0-59 (Tons)	27	(26.7)	0	0	6	(5.9)	33	32.7
III 0-19 (Years) 60-320 (Tons)	13	(12.9)	6	(5.9)	0	0	19	18.7
IV 20-80 (Years) 60-320 (Tons)	18	(17.8)	6	(5.9)	0	0	24	23.8
Total	77	(76.2)	12	(11.9)	12	(11.9)	101	100

Source: Federal Reserve Bank of Boston and the Bureau of Commercial Fisheries.

TABLE 2

DISTRIBUTION OF MASSACHUSETTS FISHING VESSELS BY AGE, SIZE, TYPE OF FISHING & GEOGRAPHICAL AREA

Universe Groundfish	Number	New Bedford	Gloucester	Gloucester-Boston	Boston	Massachusetts*	Percent
0-19 (Years) / 0-59 (Tons)	77	58 (75%)	19 (25%)	0	0	0	100
20-80 (Years) / 0-59 (Tons)	137	108 (79%)	22 (16%)	0	7 (5%)	0	100
0-19 (Years) / 60-320 (Tons)	90	43 (48%)	0	47 (52%)	0	0	100
20-80 (Years) / 60-320 (Tons)	88	24 (27%)	30 (34%)	0	34 (39%)	0	100
Total	392	233	71	47	41	0	100
Sample Groundfish							
0-19 (Years) / 0-59 (Tons)	19	11 (57.9%)	8 (42.1%)	0	0	0	100
20-80 (Years) / 0-59 (Tons)	27	20 (74.1%)	0	7 (25.9%)	0	0	100
0-19 (Years) / 60-320 (Tons)	13	6 (46.2%)	0	7 (53.8%)	0	0	100
20-80 (Years) / 60-320 (Tons)	18	5 (27.8%)	6 (33.3%)	0	7 (38.9%)	0	100
Total	77	42	14	14	7	0	100

Scallops	Massachusetts*	Other Fishing	Massachusetts*
0-19 (Years) / 60-320 (Tons)	6	0-19 / 0-59	6
20-80 (Years) / 60-320 (Tons)	6	20-80 / 0-59	6
Total	12	Total	12

Source: Federal Reserve Bank of Boston and Bureau of Commercial Fisheries.

* Excludes Boston, New Bedford and Gloucester.

gion) as the universe, it was felt that some regional breakdown within Massachusetts would be appropriate and might approximate whatever diversity exists within the universe from state to state.[3]

Great effort was taken to insure that the sample selected from each stratum (shown in Tables 1 and 2) was reasonably representative of the universe, although subject to the limitations discussed above.[4] It should be pointed out that other studies plus the Tariff Commission Investigation failed to produce any real objective information on the structure of the sample as compared to the universe.

Capital Stock, Income and Expenses

Capital assets in the fishing industry are generally of two varieties: 1) value of the vessel and equipment, and 2) cash or working capital. In many cases, the only asset carried on the balance sheet is the vessel itself. Of course, no inventories are carried under normal circumstances since the catch is sold immediately upon arrival in port.

Certificates of conditions—the source of capital data for the sample—are required by law of all corporations in Massachusetts. These statements include the assets, liabilities, and net worth for enterprises operating in the state. Income and expense data for the fishing vessels in the sample were obtained through confidential access to corporate profit and loss statements in Massachusetts.

The use of historical book value of assets presents many difficulties. First, each balance sheet reflects different prices depending on the date of acquisition of the assets. At first glance, we might think that a 25-year-old vessel would reflect 1940 prices. However, this is not generally the case. Most fishing vessels are sold often during their lifetimes and actually reflect the last purchase or resale price. Therefore, a 25-year-old vessel may actually be stated in 1964 resale prices. Although a rate of return will be computed in historical prices in the first part of this paper, a method of adjusting to constant dollars will be suggested.

---

[3] Of the 726 vessels in the universe, 505 are from Massachusetts. Thus, the regional diversity within Massachusetts is probably the predominant influence in the New England universe.

[4] Although in the strict sense this methodology violates the definition of randomness, it should be emphasized that since we know the parameters of the universe (e.g., means on tons and age) the sample may be constructed appropriately.

Gross Operating Profit and the Return on Capital

Gross operating profit is the return to the enterprise before taxes. The difficulty in calculating this profit is two-fold: 1) depreciation, and 2) excessive entrepreneurial or officer withdrawal. Thus, if assets are written off too rapidly, gross operating profit will be *understated*. Also, in small fishing firms where the stock is controlled by a few individuals, it may be common practice to compensate officers at excessive wage rates. This practice, if widespread, would tend to understate gross operating profit. Thus, one might be led on *a priori* grounds to believe that the rate of return calculated from profit and loss statements in the fishing industry may be somewhat understated.[5] A test of the entrepreneurial withdrawal hypothesis will be made later in this chapter using the data collected on officers' compensation.

The return on capital may be measured by different methods depending on the desired objective. If the purpose is to measure profitability to the owner, the owner's net worth (assets minus liabilities) may be used as an investment base (R_1). If the purpose is to judge profitability of the firm rather than the owner's return, some broader investment base must be used, such as total assets (R_2). In the latter case, the efficiency of management may be measured on the basis of total assets regardless of the source from which these assets were obtained (i.e., debt or equity). Gross operating profit or taxable income is used to compute the rate of return. A third method is to compute the rate of return on a factor of production basis. Profits are a return to equity capital while interest is a return to borrowed funds; thus, both profits and interest should be employed in computing the rate of return on total assets (R_3). All three methods will be used.[6]

---

[5] For a discussion of this problem along with empirical verification see Joseph L. McConnell, "Corporate Earnings by Size of Firm," *Survey of Current Business,* May 1945.

[6] The method by which group profit is computed is rather critical to the analysis. Since profits and losses are made within each group, they tend to cancel each other out. Thus, the yield on capital for each group will be on the average trawler. That is, $(\Sigma P/n) / (\Sigma K/n)$ where n is the number of trawlers. This is different from $\Sigma [(P/K)/n]_i$. This subtlety will affect the computations and should be recognized by the reader. The reason for the first choice is that profits were reported for firms in each group, but these firms were not identified. Thus, one could not relate profit to capital on an individual basis.

P = operating profits before taxes (taxable income)
i = interest payments
N = net worth (or equity)
K = total assets
C = officers' compensation

$$R_1 = \frac{P}{N} \qquad\qquad R_2 = \frac{P}{K} \qquad\qquad R_3 = \frac{P + i}{K}$$

A fourth rate of return may be computed by adding in officers' compensation or $\frac{P + i + C}{K} = R_4$. This statistic ($R_4$) is useful in evaluating the effect of entrepreneurial withdrawal on rates of return.

The Return on Investment, R_1 and R_2, 1962-63

As shown in Tables 1 and 2, a sample of 101 fishing vessels (enterprises) was selected from the New England universe. The sample was divided into thirteen groups for purposes of analysis. For 1963 the rate of return (before taxes) was 1.87 percent on total assets and 5.14 percent on net worth (equity) for the entire sample. This industry average does not reveal the wide dispersion in the rate of return across groups. On the total asset base, the rate of return varies from 13.08 percent to −11.07 percent. Net worth, being a smaller base, naturally shows greater dispersion as rates of return vary from 38.82 percent to −69.36 percent. Tables 3 and 4 show the financial experience for the New England fishing industry for 1962 and 1963. For 1962, the dispersion in the rates of return was even greater as they ranged from 32.96 to −20.92 and 133.79 to −296.56 percent on total assets and net worth, respectively. The rate of return on assets and net worth for the entire sample for 1962 was .42 and 1.20 percent respectively. Thus, it is quite evident that earnings within the industry are hardly uniform. However, this may reasonably be expected in many industries where the dispersion in rates of return reflect differences in entrepreneurial talent, etc. Many segments of the industry show rates of return comparable with high returns earned in other industries.

The overall rate of return in the New England fishing industry is decidedly below the return in other segments of the U.S. economy including the combined sector of agriculture, forestry and fishing (see Table 5). Thus, when compared to the primary industries, the rate of return in New England fishing is still below its counterparts.

TABLE 3

FINANCIAL EXPERIENCE OF FISHING ENTERPRISES IN NEW ENGLAND, 1963

Group	Size (Tons)	Age (Years)	Type of Fishing	Region	No. in Group	Total Assets $	Net Worth $	Total Taxable Income* $	Total Taxable Income $ ÷ Total Assets	Total Taxable Income $ ÷ Net Worth	Assets Per Vessel $	Crew	Assets Per Crewman $	No. of Firms with Loss	No. of Firms with Profit
1	0-59	0-19	GF	G	8	171,254.40	120,696.08	613.16	0.358%	0.508%	21,406.80	37	4,628.49	3	5
2	0-59	0-19	GF	NB	11	218,396.62	83,598.26	(17,717.59)	− 8.110%	−21.190%	19,854.15	54	4,044.36	8	3
3	0-59	0-19	O	Mass.	6	197,155.11	55,862.87	(2,143.41)	− 1.090%	− 3.837%	32,842.52	40	4,926.37	5	1
4	60-x	0-19	GF	G-B	7	890,606.24	346,012.27	27,325.87	3.070%	7.897%	127,229.46	89	10,006.81	3	4
5	60-x	0-19	GF	NB	6	355,811.51	203,933.35	34,939.99	9.820%	1.713%	59,301.92	43	8,274.68	1	5
6	60-x	0-19	S	Mass.	6	345,229.43	111,354.53	(3,324.20)	− 0.963%	− 2.985%	57,538.24	67	5,152.67	3	3
7	0-59	20-80	GF	G-B	7	44,243.25	9,795.73	(2,345.97)	− 5.302%	−23.949%	6,320.46	30	1,474.76	4	3
8	0-59	20-80	GF	NB	20	411,787.66	72,480.11	(21,984.67)	− 5.339%	−30.330%	20,589.38	100	4,117.87	12	8
9	0-59	20-80	O	Mass.	6	92,940.13	14,835.00	(10,283.99)	−11.070%	−69.360%	15,490.02	32	2,904.38	4	2
10	60-x	20-80	GF	B	6	289,318.51	97,451.79	37,833.28	13.077%	38.820%	41,331.22	90	3,214.65	3	4
11	60-x	20-80	GF	G	6	184,649.96	93,332.62	19,712.43	10.676%	21.120%	30,774.99	54	3,419.44	3	3
12	60-x	20-80	GF	NB	5	165,463.68	34,867.12	(1,762.12)	− 1.065%	− 5.056%	33,092.74	37	4,471.99	2	3
13	60-x	20-80	S	Mass.	6	256,422.18	75,063.87	7,000.24	2.730%	9.326%	42,737.03	66	3,885.18	2	4
Total all Groups					101	3,623,177.68	1,319,283.60	67,857.22	1.874%	5.143%	35,873.05	739	4,902.81	53	48

Source: Federal Reserve Bank of Boston; Bureau of Commercial Fisheries; **Certificates of Condition,** The Commonwealth Massachusetts, and special tabulations of group income tax returns by the staff of the Department of Corporations and Taxation, The Commonwealth of Massachusetts.

Code:

G = Gloucester
N.B. = New Bedford
G-B = Gloucester and Boston
Mass. = Excludes Boston,
        New Bedford and Gloucester

GF = Groundfish
S = Scallops
O = Other fishing
* = Parentheses indicate loss

TABLE 4

FINANCIAL EXPERIENCE OF FISHING ENTERPRISES IN NEW ENGLAND, 1962

Group	Size (Tons)	Age (Years)	Type of Fishing	Region	No. in Group	Total Assets $	Net Worth $	Total Taxable Income* $	Total Taxable Income $ ÷ Total Assets	Total Taxable Income $ ÷ Net Worth	Assets Per Vessel $	Crew	Assets Per Crewman $	No. of Firms with Loss	No. of Firms with Profit
1	0-59	0-19	GF	G	7	153,409.82	107,422.67	4,251.79	2.772%	3.958%	21,915.69	33	4,648.78	4	3
2	0-59	0-19	GF	NB	9	218,026.14	79,561.57	(16,416.27)	-7.529%	-20.630%	24,225.13	45	4,845.03	7	2
3	0-59	0-19	O	Mass.	5	83,915.53	8,526.21	(12,423.63)	-14.805%	-145.700%	16,783.11	32	2,622.36	5	0
4	60-x	0-19	GF	G-B	7	926,162.45	359,069.25	12,601.06	1.361%	3.509%	132,308.92	89	10,406.32	3	4
5	60-x	0-19	GF	NB	6	394,705.45	189,021.26	6,944.82	1.759%	3.674%	65,784.24	43	9,179.20	2	4
6	60-x	0-19	S	Mass.	6	380,089.53	117,956.68	(18,494.41)	-4.866%	-15.680%	63,348.26	67	5,672.98	4	2
7	0-59	20-80	GF	G-B	6	36,140.06	11,902.08	(489.98)	-1.356%	-4.117%	6,023.34	26	1,390.00	4	2
8	0-59	20-80	GF	NB	19	395,486.99	101,971.49	(49,634.81)	-10.780%	-41.810%	20,815.10	95	4,163.02	15	4
9	0-59	20-80	O	Mass.	6	92,428.71	6,520.62	(19,337.47)	-20.921%	-296.560%	15,404.79	32	2,888.40	6	0
10	60-x	20-80	GF	B	7	276,229.08	68,057.45	91,055.75	32.964%	133.790%	39,461.13	90	3,069.21	2	5
11	60-x	20-80	GF	G	6	188,236.36	97,996.15	3,845.50	2.043%	3.924%	31,372.73	54	3,485.86	3	3
12	60-x	20-80	GF	NB	5	153,348.37	38,259.98	(8,767.56)	-5.717%	-22.916%	30,669.67	37	4,144.55	2	3
13	60-x	20-80	S	Mass.	5	231,425.78	53,688.31	(15,076.04)	-6.514%	-28.080%	46,285.16	55	4,207.74	3	2
Total all Groups					94	3,529,604.27	1,239,953.72	14,941.25	0.423%	1.200%	37,548.98	698	5,056.78	60	34

Source: Federal Reserve Bank of Boston; Bureau of Commercial Fisheries; **Certificates of Condition,** The Commonwealth Massachusetts, and special tabulations of group income tax returns by the staff of the Department of Corporations and Taxation, The Commonwealth of Massachusetts.

*Parentheses indicate loss.

Code:
G = Gloucester;
NB = New Bedford;
G-B = Gloucester and Boston;
Mass. = Excludes Boston,
New Bedford and Gloucester

GF = Groundfish
S = Scallops
O = Other fishing

One may argue that such results may be obtained in any 2 years especially since profits are so volatile from year to year. This is a serious criticism. However, the results do not conflict with previous studies by the Tariff Commission and others of profitability in the industry.[7] Although these studies did not employ an investment base (criticized earlier) they did show that the industry as a whole experienced losses from 1953-1957 which would obviously produce a negative return on a positive investment base.

TABLE 5

COMPARISON OF RATES OF RETURN IN FISHING AND OTHER INDUSTRY GROUPINGS, 1963 and 1962

		New England Fishing	Range	U.S. Ag., For.&Fish.	U.S. Mfg.	All U.S. Economy
P/K	63	1.87	13.08—(— 11.07)	3.10	8.70	3.70
	62	.42	32.96—(— 20.92)	2.40	8.20	3.60
P/N	63	5.14	38.82—(— 69.36)	n.a.	18.40	n.a.
	62	1.20	133.79—(—296.56)	4.70	12.80	10.80

Source: Federal Reserve Bank of Boston; **Statistics of Income,** Internal Revenue Service; **Quarterly Financial Report,** Federal Trade Commission and Securities and Exchange Commission.

What is significant about the results is that some segments of the New England industry apparently earned a fair or competitive return on investment. In the postwar period, the cost associated with fishing has risen rapidly. However, because of increased imports, fish prices have not increased appreciably. These forces have produced a squeeze on profits in the New England industry. However, some firms have still survived and managed to earn a rate of return high enough to hold some capital in the fishing industry.

Total Factor Returns Including Officers' Compensation, R_3 and R_4

As discussed earlier, a third rate of return including interest payments may be computed. This represents the total factor returns since profits may be viewed as return on equity while interest payments are a return on borrowed capital employed by the enterprise. Stigler takes this approach in computing rates of return in manufacturing.[8] Of course, the resulting rate of return will reflect whatever difference in debt structure plus interest rates exists across indus-

[7] U.S. Tariff Commission and Lynch, Doherty, Draheim, *op. cit.*
[8] George J. Stigler, *Capital and Rates of Return in Manufacturing Industries.* (National Bureau of Economic Research, New York, 1963).

tries. Interest payments were obtained only for 1963. This was the only year a complete breakdown of revenue and expenses was possible without considerably more work by the Department of Corporations and Taxation which supplied these data.

As indicated in Table 6, the inclusion of interest payments raises the rate of return from 1.87 percent (Table 5) to 4.28 percent on total assets. This adjustment has the effect of narrowing the rate of return differential between the New England fishing industry and the other sectors shown. The New England fishing industry in 1963 had a debt structure (i.e., the ratio of debt to total assets) of 63.6 percent compared to 49.4 percent, 36.0 percent, and 66.3 percent in Agriculture-Forestry-Fishing; U.S. Manufacturing and all U.S. industries, respectively. Table 7 shows the impact by group when interest is included as part of the total factor returns.

TABLE 6

COMPARISON OF THE TOTAL FACTOR RATE OF RETURN IN FISHING AND OTHER INDUSTRY GROUPINGS, 1963

	New England Fishing	Range	U.S. Ag., For.&Fish.	U.S. Mfg.	All U.S. Economy
(P+i)/ K	4.28	13.64–(−8.49)	4.70	9.50	5.00
(P + i + C) / K	13.90	—	7.80	11.30	6.20

Source: Federal Reserve Bank of Boston; **Statistics of Income,** Internal Revenue Service.

If officers' compensation is added as a return to the investment base, the New England fishing industry has a rate of return of 13.9 percent which greatly exceeds even that return (with officers' compensation) in all manufacturing. In 1963, officers of the 101 fishing enterprises obtained compensation of $347,537.99 (compared to profit before taxes of $67,857.22) which averages approximately $3500 per enterprise. In the fishing industry there are usually three nominal officers per enterprise whose names are listed on the Certificate of Condition. Although the inclusion of officers' compensation does raise the rate of return (P + i + C)/K above that earned in manufacturing, it would be dangerous to conclude that salary withdrawals are excessive in the fishing industry. Even if each enterprise had only one full-time officer, $3500 per year does not seem excessive for such responsibility. However, the problem in the fishing industry is more complicated since the officer is usually the captain of the vessel. Under most contracts, the captain receives 10 percent of

TABLE 7

OTHER RATES OF RETURN ON ASSETS AND NET WORTH, 1963

(1) Interest and Profits (Before Taxes)   (2) Profits (After Taxes)

Group	Size	Age	Type of Fishing	Region	Number in Group	Total Taxable Income	Interest payments	(1) Rate of Return on Assets*	Income After Taxes†	(2) Rate of Return on Assets (after taxes)*	(2) Rate of Return on Net Worth (after taxes)*
1	0-59	0-19	GF	G	8	613.16	2,006.56	1.53%	418.18	0.24%	3.46%
2	0-59	0-19	GF	N.B.	11	(17,717.59)	4,703.34	− 5.96%	(17,717.59)	− 8.11%	−21.19%
3	0-59	0-19	O	Mass.	6	(2,143.41)	8,141.30	3.04%	(2,143.41)	− 1.09%	− 3.84%
4	60-x	0-19	GF	G-B	7	27,325.87	19,907.13	5.30%	18,636.24	2.09%	5.39%
5	60-x	0-19	GF	N.B.	6	34,939.99	6,925.84	11.77%	23,829.07	6.70%	11.68%
6	60-x	0-19	S	Mass.	6	(3,324.20)	15,844.41	3.63%	(3,324.20)	− 0.96%	− 2.99%
7	0-59	20-80	GF	G-B	7	(2,345.97)	611.06	− 3.92%	(2,345.97)	− 5.30%	−23.95%
8	0-59	20-80	GF	N.B.	20	(21,984.67)	5,749.72	− 3.94%	(21,984.67)	− 5.34%	−30.33%
9	0-59	20-80	O	Mass.	6	(10,288.99)	2,398.60	− 8.49%	(10,288.99)	−11.07%	−69.36%
10	60-x	20-80	GF	B	7	37,833.28	1,641.37	13.64%	25,803.30	8.92%	26.48%
11	60-x	20-80	GF	G	6	19,712.43	2,479.43	12.02%	13,443.88	7.28%	14.40%
12	60-x	20-80	GF	N.B.	5	(1,762.92)	6,417.66	2.81%	(1,762.92)	− 1.07%	− 5.06%
13	60-x	20-80	S	Mass.	6	7,000.24	10,293.91	6.74%	4,774.16	1.86%	6.36%

*Total assets and net worth bases may be found in Table 3.
†Tax rate = 31.8% (Federal and State of Massachusetts combined).

Code: G = Gloucester   GF = Groundfish
        N.B. = New Bedford   S = Scallops
        G-B = Gloucester and Boston   O = Other fishing
        Mass. = Excludes Boston,
                 New Bedford and Gloucester

Source: Federal Reserve Bank of Boston; Bureau of Commercial Fisheries; **Certificate of Condition,** The Commonwealth of Massachusetts, and special tabulations of group income tax returns by the staff of the Department of Corporations Taxation, The Commonwealth of Massachusetts.

the vessel's gross share and is thus compensated twice; once for his position as captain, and a second time as officer of the enterprise. Obviously, the captain-officer makes decisions concerning the vessel which cannot be neatly separated into one function (officer) or another (captain). McConnell's investigations of such data for the 1931-41 period showed that for fisheries there was no evidence of significant decrease in profits by the payment of excessive officers' compensation.[9] One way of adjusting for excessive withdrawals would be to compute the total compensation for the officer-captain (share of the value of the catch plus officer's compensation) and compare this to the market rate for such skills (for example, to semi-professional or executive personnel). Any excess over the market rate would be considered a return to capital, and not labor.

The Cross-sectional Nature of the Rate of Return, 1963

The existence of a wide dispersion in the rate of return across groups in the New England fishing industry poses many fascinating questions:

> 1) Is this dispersion or variation in the rate of return related to any technological factors such as size of the vessel (scale) or capital-labor ratio? If so, is there an optimum size and combination of capital and labor?

> 2) Is the dispersion of rates of return a function of the type of fishing, port of operation or age of vessel?

> 3) Is the dispersion in the rate of return due to more efficient use of inputs such as repair, maintenance and administrative expenses?

These questions will be explored in this section. However, we must briefly describe the data employed. Data were taken from corporation tax returns. These returns require the corporation to list the following specific expenses:

1. Compensation of Officers	7. Rents
2. Repairs	8. Advertising
3. Taxes	9. Other Deductions
4. Interest	10. Salaries and Wages
5. Depreciation	11. Pension and other
6. Bad Debts	Employee Benefits

[9] McConnell, *op. cit.*

Although most of the above expenses are readily identifiable as those incurred by the vessel, some special problems are associated with the reporting of expenses in fishing industry. First, salaries and wages may be gross (before deduction of those items labor must pay from its share) or net. Second, the category, *other deductions,* may include those items normally paid from labor's share, but as an administrative matter, paid by the vessel. Third, some vessel owners report only their vessel share and neglect to report gross stock and fishermen's wages. In order to arrange these expenses in a functional breakdown, the following check procedure was employed along with some estimation where necessary.

Functional Breakdown of Revenue and Costs

 1. Gross Stock   (GS)
 2. Less Joint Expenses   (JC)
 3. Net Revenue   (TRn)
 4. Less Labor's Share   (WL)
 5. Vessel Share   (VS)
 6. Add Other Income   (O)
 7. Less Fixed Expenses (8-14)   (FC)
 8. Compensation of Officers   (C)
 9. Repair and Maintenance   (R)
10. Taxes   (T)
11. Interest   (i)
12. Depreciation   (D)
13. Administrative (Bad Debts; Rents; Advertising)   (A)
14. Insurance and Other Deductions   (I+x)

Gross stock was obtained from the Bureau of Commercial Fisheries as a check on gross receipts shown on corporate income tax returns. The Bureau's figures were used in all cases where reported receipts diverged from actual receipts. However, all divergencies could be explained on the basis of only reporting vessel share or income. Joint expenses and labor's share were estimated by using union contracts in Boston, New Bedford and Gloucester. In addition, an informal agreement known as the Italian lay was used for a few nonunion vessels operating out of Gloucester. Other vessel income (excluding capital gains) and fixed expenses (8-13) were taking directly from income tax returns. Other deductions (14) represent the residual or difference between vessel income (5 and 6) minus fixed expenses (8-13) and whatever profit or loss was made by the group.

This procedure organizes the information into meaningful categories and also seeks to clear up any ambiguities inherent in the income tax returns themselves. Union regulations make it easy to estimate, for example, joint cost or labor share since these items are expressly stated in the union contract. Each vessel in our sample was designated to be under a union contract in one of the ports or on the Italian lay in Gloucester. In some cases, joint expenses were estimated from other industry information obtained from vessel owners in the particular area. This procedure must be employed when working with standard tax returns for the industry. The one drawback in the case of fishing industry is that hull and liability insurance are not reported separately but must be included in our residual category (number 14). However, insurance would undoubtedly be the largest component of this category which would also include office supplies, phone bills, and other administrative expenses plus whatever fishing gear and supplies (not paid by labor) are used up in the course of the year. According to Vaughn, Doherty and Draheim, hull insurance and protection and indemnity insurance for New Bedford trawlers have recently averaged $7000 per year. On 101 trawlers this would be $707,000 which is 64% of the residual category.

In order to analyze the rate of return across groups the following identity is useful:

$$\frac{P}{K} = \frac{TR}{K} - \frac{VC}{K} - \frac{FC}{K}$$

Where TR is the gross stock and other income, VC variable cost (joint expenses plus labor's share) and FC fixed cost (8-14). Fixed cost may be further broken down into its components:

$$\frac{FC}{K} = \frac{C}{K} + \frac{R}{K} + \frac{T}{K} + \frac{i}{K} + \frac{D}{K} + \frac{A}{K} + \frac{I+x}{K}$$

Altogether, we have nine general components (plus sub-components) of the rate of return on total assets. The same procedure may be carried out for net worth (N). It is our purpose to correlate the individual components with P/K to see which ones are highly correlated with the rate of return. In this way, we may determine which expenses are significantly related to the dispersion in the rate of return. The question is just how the components of the rate of return (e.g., C/K) move with the overall rate of return across groups.

*Correlation Matrix
of Rate of Return with its
Various Sub-components**

Simple Correlation

P/K	with	GS/K	+.246
		JC/K	−.125
		TR$_n$/K	+.292
		WL/K	+.343
		VS/K	+.178
		O/K	+.025
		(VS+O)/K	+.159
		FC/K	−.019
		C/K	−.072
		R/K	−.508
		T/K	+.166
		i/K	−.268
		D/K	−.416
		A/K	−.365
		(I+x)/K	+.348

*See Functional Breakdown of Revenue and Cost

From the magnitude of the simple correlation coefficients, it appears that the four leading expenses, repair, maintenance, depreciation, and administrative, are inversely related to the rate of return on investment. This means that where the expenses are highest, the rate of return is lowest. However, none of these coefficients is significant at the 5 percent level. Fixed costs as a category are not significantly related to the rate of return ($r = -.019$). Thus, the fixed costs per unit of capital employed is amazingly constant across groups and fails to "vary" with variations in P/K. Groups earning high rates of return seem to generate more revenue per unit of capital (GS/K). However, the correlation coefficient is fairly low ($r = +.246$) and further, the analysis failed to reveal a high correlation between the rate of return and any one of its components. But the composite influence of all the components must explain the total variation in the rate of return. The only possible conclusion is that highly profitable groups generate more income per unit of capital although their fixed cost per unit of capital is about the same or a little less than the less profitable groups.

TABLE 8

RELATION BETWEEN RATE OF RETURN AND VESSEL CHARACTERISTICS FOR NEW ENGLAND FISHING ENTERPRISES, 1963

Number of Group	Rate of Return on Total Assets	Size		Age		Type of Fishing			Region				
		0-59	60-X	0-19	20-80	Groundfish	Scallopers	Other	Boston	Gloucester	New Bedford	Mass.*	Boston and Gloucester
10	13.077%		X		X	X			X				
11	10.676%		X		X	X				X			
5	9.820%		X	X		X					X		
4	3.070%		X	X		X							X
13	2.730%		X		X		X			X			
1	.358%	X		X		X						X	
6	− .963%		X	X			X					X	
12	− 1.065%		X		X		X					X	
3	− 1.090%		X	X		X					X		
7	− 5.302%	X			X			X			X		
8	− 5.339%	X			X	X					X		
2	− 8.110%	X		X		X					X		
9	+11.070%	X			X			X					X

Number of Group	Rate of Return on Equity	Size		Age		Type of Fishing			Region				
		0-59	60-X	0-19	20-80	Groundfish	Scallopers	Other	Boston	Gloucester	New Bedford	Mass.*	Boston and Gloucester
10	38.820%		X		X	X			X				
11	21.120%		X		X	X				X			
5	17.133%		X	X		X					X		
13	9.326%		X		X		X			X			
4	7.987%		X	X		X							X
1	.508%	X		X		X						X	
6	− 2.985%		X	X			X					X	
3	− 3.837%		X	X		X					X		
12	− 5.056%		X		X		X					X	
2	−21.190%	X		X		X					X		
7	−23.949%	X			X			X			X		
8	−30.330%	X			X	X					X		
9	−69.360%	X			X			X					X

Source: Federal Reserve Bank of Boston; derived from Table 3.
* Excludes Boston, New Bedford and Gloucester.

TABLE 9

RELATION BETWEEN RATE OF RETURN AND VESSEL CHARACTERISTICS FOR NEW ENGLAND FISHING ENTERPRISES, 1962

Number of Group	Rate of Return on Total Assets	Size 0-59	Size 60-X	Age 0-19	Age 20-80	Groundfish	Scallopers	Other	Boston	Gloucester	New Bedford	Mass.*	Boston and Gloucester
10	32.964%		X		X	X			X				
1	2.772%	X		X		X				X			
11	2.043%		X		X	X				X			
5	1.759%		X	X		X					X		
4	1.361%		X	X		X							X
7	1.356%	X			X	X							X
6	− 4.866%	X		X			X					X	
12	− 5.717%		X		X	X					X		
13	− 6.514%		X		X	X	X				X		
2	− 7.529%	X		X		X					X		
8	− 10.780%	X			X	X					X		
3	− 14.805%	X		X				X				X	
9	− 20.921%	X			X			X				X	

Rate of Return to Equity

Number of Group	Rate of Return to Equity	Size 0-59	Size 60-X	Age 0-19	Age 20-80	Groundfish	Scallopers	Other	Boston	Gloucester	New Bedford	Mass.*	Boston and Gloucester
10	133.790%		X		X	X			X				
1	3.958%	X		X		X				X			
11	3.924%		X		X	X				X			
5	3.674%		X	X		X					X		
4	3.509%		X	X		X							X
7	− 4.117%	X			X	X							X
6	− 15.680%	X		X			X					X	
2	− 20.630%	X		X		X					X		
12	− 22.916%		X		X	X					X		
13	− 28.080%		X		X	X	X				X		
8	− 41.810%	X			X	X					X		
3	−145.700%	X		X				X				X	
9	−296.560%	X			X			X				X	

Source: Federal Reserve Bank of Boston; derived from Table 4.
* Excludes Boston, New Bedford and Gloucester.

The Rate of Return and Vessel Size

Miernyk and Rosen show in their study of the Boston fleet that the profitability of individual trawlers depends to a considerable extent on their ability to spend a large number of days at sea each year.[10] The authors further show a strong rank correlation between size (gross tons) and earnings (1953: .73; 1954: .83; 1955; .63). As trawlers reach capacity levels, both overhead and direct costs (since the latter also include some fixed cost) fall as a percent of total revenue.

Table 8 demonstrates the relationship between the rate of return and the various characteristics of the sample for 1963. A strong correlation exists between vessel size and the rate of return on total assets as well as equity. The leading five groups with the highest return on assets are all vessels over 60 tons while the bottom five groups are below 60 tons in size. The same relationship seems to prevail for 1962, although group 1 (0-59 tons) moved from 6th place to 2nd. However, the rank correlation of groups (rate of return on total assets) from 1962 to 1963 is .824 which is statistically significant at the 1 percent level. No clear relationship is apparent between age and the rate of return. Moreover, the five leading groups were engaged in groundfishing which is reported to be a depressed segment of the fishing industry. Table 9 presents the results for 1962.

A dummy variable (S) may be used to show the statistical significance of the relation of vessel size to the rate of return.

S = dummy variable 0 = large vessels 1 = small vessels

$$1963 \quad P/K = .0533 \quad - \quad .1043 \text{ S} \qquad R^2 = .546$$
$$(.0265)$$
$$-3.636$$

$$P/N = .1232 \quad - \quad .37016 \text{ S} \qquad R^2 = .497$$
$$(.11224)$$
$$-3.2978$$

Both regression coefficients are statistically significant at the 1 percent level. The coefficients indicate that large vessels average 5.33 percent on assets (the *intercept* of the regression function) while small vessels average 10.43 percent less than large vessels (the *slope* of the regression function) or −5.10 percent. The same interpretation

[10] W. K. Miernyk and Sumner Rosen, *The Economics of Freezing Fish at Sea*, Northeastern University, 1957 unpublished report prepared for United States Fish and Wildlife Service.

is true of the return on equity. The relation of vessel size to the rate of return on capital is extremely significant.

It should be pointed out that although excessive salary withdrawals may produce a downward bias for the industry as a whole, they do not seem to be related to vessel size in our cross sectional analysis. That is, one may argue that small vessels are usually family enterprises while larger vessels may be owned by processors, wholesalers or larger fleet owners. Therefore, excessive compensation of officers may produce the differential rate of return across groups. In order to test this hypothesis, officers' compensation per unit of capital was correlated with vessel size (dummy variable) as in the above equations.

$$C/K = .100 + \underset{\substack{(.07773) \\ 1.0496}}{.08159 \text{ S}} \qquad R^2 = .09$$

$$C/N = .248 + \underset{\substack{(.35720) \\ 1.3979}}{.49935 \text{ S}} \qquad R^2 = .15$$

Neither regression coefficient is statistically significant at the 5 percent level. However, the positive sign of the regression coefficient indicates that compensation of officers per unit of capital may be somewhat higher for small vessels.

Unfortunately, the entire analysis does not go far enough. The more fundamental question is why vessel size might be a factor affecting the rate of return. As indicated by Miernyk and Rosen, larger vessels make more trips and spend more days at sea per year than the smaller, less profitable vessels.[11] In addition, time is an important variable in this entire analysis. We are talking in essence about the rate of return per annum. Therefore, smaller vessels may be idle a larger part of the year, for example owing to adverse weather conditions, while the larger vessels are free to operate. This would be an economy of scale resulting from seasonal factors.

Van Meir's recent study of the Boston fleet indicates that high earning vessels make more trips and spend more days at sea per year, (1960-63).[12] He says, "The combination of greater landings and slightly higher average price for the higher earning vessels yielded average gross sales per year of $258,966 — 46 percent greater than gross sales of $177,598 realized by the lower earning vessels." How-

[11] Miernyk and Rosen, *op. cit.*
[12] Lawrence Van Mier, "A New England Groundfish Case History," (unpublished paper, 1965).

ever, Lynch, *et al.* state, "Thus size, although an important consideration in the analysis of the Boston trawler fleet, should not be overemphasized, and must be viewed in relation to other factors."[13] The authors go on to state that managerial skill of the vessel captain may be an important consideration leading to higher earnings. This may imply that vessel captains with the greatest skill and experience would naturally gravitate to larger vessels. Thus, size may mask this tendency. If the captain receives a fixed percentage of the catch, the incentive would be to captain a larger vessel where this dollar share would certainly be greater. It is very probable that the "best captains" are also running larger, more profitable vessels. Only through a controlled experiment can an assessment be made of the influence of other factors such as the size of the vessel while holding the managerial factor constant.

The reader should recognize that all large vessels do not make profits. In fact, many large vessels experienced an operating loss. Table 10 shows the relationship between vessel size categories and the incidence of profit (loss). Seventeen of the large vessels actually experienced losses. However, the incidence of profit *was not independent of vessel size.* The chi-square test on the null hypothesis of independence was rejected at the 5 percent level.

Total Revenue, Variable and Fixed Costs and Their Relation to Vessel Size

The hypothesis emerging from previous studies plus our own analysis is that profitability may depend at least in part on vessel size.[14] However, the rate of return on invested capital (total assets) is influenced by three general components: 1) total revenue; 2) variable costs; and 3) fixed cost. In order to be comparable with the rate of return, these components must be placed on a per unit of capital basis:

$$\frac{P}{K} = \frac{TR}{K} - \frac{VC}{K} - \frac{FC}{K}$$

Larger vessels may generate more revenue per unit of capital, and/or be more efficient in the utilization of inputs. This will give them a higher rate of return on invested capital.[15]

---

[13] Lynch, Doherty and Draheim, *op. cit.*

[14] Miernyk and Rosen, *op. cit.*

[15] VC is composed of joint expenses plus labor's share. Labor's share is, of course, a function of total revenue and would probably be higher for a vessel generating greater revenue per unit of capital employed. However, differences in the "lay" or joint cost across groups (i.e., large to small) might contribute to a differential rate of return.

TABLE 10

TEST OF INDEPENDENCE OF VESSEL SIZE AND INCIDENCE OF PROFIT (LOSSES)

Vessel Size	Number of Vessels Making * Profits	Losses	Total
Large	26 (20.4)	17 (22.4)	43
Small	22 (27.6)	36 (30.1)	58
Total	48	53	101

*Theoretical or expected frequency is shown in parentheses. $X^2 = 5.10$.
Source: Special tabulation of group income tax returns, by the staff of the Department of Corporations and Taxation, Commonwealth of Massachusetts.

Group Averages: Rate of Return on Total Assets

Vessel Classification	P/K	TR/K	VC/K	FC/K
Large Vessels	.05334	2.98302	2.01665	.91303
Small Vessels	−.05092	2.61760	1.74870	.91981

From the information presented above, it is apparent that large vessels generate more revenue per unit of capital than smaller vessels. This automatically makes VC/K higher since labor (a large component of variable cost) receives a fixed percentage of the revenue per unit of capital generated. FC/K is slightly higher for smaller vessels and accounts for less than 1 percentage point difference in the rate of return between large and small vessels. That is, we may partition the components of the rate of return in order to discover which are more significant in explaining the difference in earnings between large and small vessels.

	Large	Small	Difference
TR/K	2.98302	2.61763	.36539
VC/K	2.01665	1.74874	.26791
Net Revenue/K	.96637	.86889	.09748
FC/K	.91303	.91981	−.00678
Difference	.05334	−.05092	.10426

The conclusion reached is that approximately 93 percent of the difference in the rate of return (.09748/.10426) between groups (i.e., large versus small) *is due to the superior income generating power of large vessels.* This conclusion is consistent with that reached by Miernyk and Rosen.[16] Why do larger vessels generate more revenue per unit of capital employed? There are four possible answers to this question:

Larger vessels when compared to smaller vessels

(1) make more trips per year

(2) spend a greater number of days at sea per trip

(3) yield greater capital productivity per day at sea

(4) receive higher average prices.

Points (1) and (2) may be considered as differences in factor utilization per unit of time. If capital and labor are utilized more days per year on large as compared to small vessels, the per annum rate of return will be higher assuming costs do not increase appreciably with this greater utilization. Point (3) may be considered an economy of scale.[17] Larger vessels may also obtain a higher price for their fish. This may be due to numerous factors such as storage facilities, links with large buyers and vessel operations during periods of the year such as winter-months when prices are high. Of course all of these factors may be considered economies of scale. If we consider points (1) to (4) to reflect basic economies of scale in the operation of a fishing enterprise, we may attempt to measure their combined influence.[18]

A Production Function for a Fishing Enterprise

One way to establish a production function for the fishing enterprise is to make adjustments to the data for some of the factors considered in the last section. Let us use the following symbols: (all variables on a per vessel basis.)

S_d = days at sea per trip

T = number of trips per year

P = average price received during the year

Q = landings (in pounds) per year

K = capital or total assets employed during year

L = labor or number in the crew per year

PQ = revenue per year

---

[16] Miernyk and Rosen, *op. cit.*

[17] Capital productivity per day at sea may be higher due to the utilization of a very labor intensive technology. In the above case, we are assuming a constant capital-labor ratio where scale of operations makes a difference in factor productivity.

[18] Data are not readily available on number of fishing days, trips made and pounds landed for the 1963 sample of 101 fishing enterprises.

Let the days at sea per year be the "utilization factor" or $U = S_d T$
If all vessels spend the same number of days at sea per year, the
"utilization factor" will not affect vessel value productivity per
year. However, value productivity per vessel may be affected by
the distribution of the days at sea over the 12 months of the year.
This will affect average price received for the year and possibly
factor productivity since even large vessels are probably not as
physically productive in rough winter weather. We may specify
the following Cobb-Douglas production function for the fishing
enterprise.[19]

$$PQ = A K^{\alpha} L^{\beta} U^{\gamma}$$

"U" is the utilization factor placed in the equation to adjust the
variables for the greater number of days capital and labor are used
on large as opposed to smaller vessels. Let "Z" represent the influence of price on total revenue, as large vessels may land more of
their catch during times of the year when price is high.

$$PQ = A K^{\alpha} L^{\beta} (U Z)^{\gamma}$$

If we assume that no economies of scale exist except those in "U"
and "Z" (i.e., none associated with capital-labor productivity per
day at sea) then the economies of scale discussed in U and Z may
be represented by the following dummy variable:

$$0 = \text{Large Vessel}$$
$$1 = \text{Small Vessel}$$
$$S = \text{Size-dummy variable}$$
$$UZ = S$$

Thus, the Cobb-Douglas production function may be written in the
following way (unconstrained and constrained):

$$PQ = A K^{\alpha} L^{\beta} S^{\gamma} \qquad \text{or} \qquad \frac{PQ}{K} = A \left(\frac{K}{L} \right)^{\alpha} S^{\gamma}$$

[19] P. H. Douglas, "Are There Laws of Production?", *The American Economic
Review*, Vol. 38, (1948), pp. 1-41. Since capital and labor employed by the
fishing firm generate only value-added, the latter might be a better measure of
output. The data indicate the ratio of value-added (wages, profits and depreciation) is fairly constant across groups. Therefore, total revenue and value-added
will yield approximately the same elasticities in the Cobb-Douglas function. In
addition, our interest in economies of scale which affect revenue per enterprise
makes the latter a better measure of production.

The following production functions for the fishing vessel were estimated using the data presented in Table 11.

1. *Cobb-Douglas: Unadjusted for UZ*

$$\text{Log PQ} = 5.5702 + \underset{\substack{(.2673)\\3.7497}}{1.0026} \ \text{Log L} + \underset{\substack{(.1453)\\2.4997}}{.3631} \ \text{Log K}$$

$R^2 = .914 \qquad F = 53.43 \qquad N = 13$

2. *Cobb-Douglas: Adjusted for UZ*

$$\text{Log PQ} = 7.1617 + \underset{\substack{(.2954)\\1.6691}}{.4931} \ \text{Log L} + \underset{\substack{(.1185)\\2.779}}{.3293} \ \text{Log K} - \underset{\substack{(.1959)\\-2.536}}{.4969} \ \text{S}$$

$R^2 = .949 \qquad F = 56.32 \qquad N = 13$

3. *Cobb-Douglas (Linear): Unadjusted for UZ* [20]

$$\text{Log} \left(\frac{PQ}{L}\right) = 5.1833 + \underset{\substack{(.1500)\\3.309}}{.4966} \ \text{Log} \left(\frac{K}{L}\right)$$

$R^2 = .4957 \qquad N = 13$

4. *Cobb-Douglas (Linear): Adjusted for UZ*

$$\text{Log} \left(\frac{PQ}{L}\right) = 6.8506 + \underset{\substack{(.1127)\\2.8206}}{.3179} \ \text{Log} \left(\frac{K}{L}\right) - \underset{\substack{(.1020)\\-3.745}}{.3821} \ \text{S}$$

$R^2 = .787 \qquad F = 18.546 \qquad N = 13$

The results indicate that in the production of landed fish the size of the vessel is a significant determinant of both labor and capital value productivity (PQ/L; PQ/K). All estimated coefficients except in Case 2 for labor input (L) are statistically significant at the 5 percent level. Case 1 illustrates significant economies of scale accruing as a 1 percent increase in factor inputs results in a 1.3657 percent increase in output. In Case 2, the Cobb-Douglas is adjusted for a UZ shift in the production function. After increases in factor input (ie., capital and labor) are accounted for, large vessels

[20]A linear Cobb-Douglas means that the production function is assumed to be linear homogeneous; therefore, the exponents on capital and labor *always* sum to unity. In this case, we are assuming no economies of scale expressly due to increases in factor inputs.

Scatter Diagram I

RELATION OF CREW VALUE PRODUCTIVITY TO CAPITAL INTENSITY AND VESSEL SIZE
(dollars)

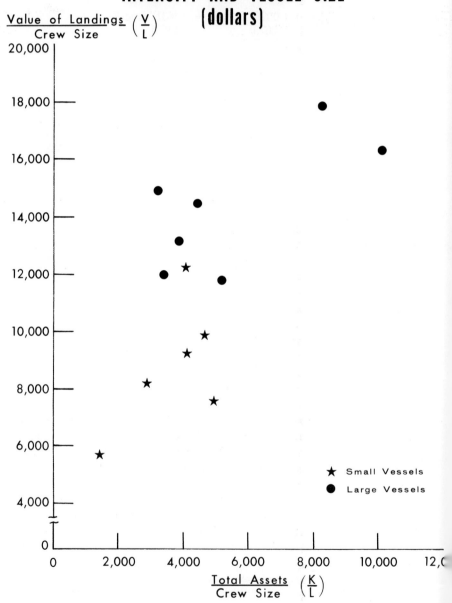

Source: Table 11

TABLE 11

MAJOR PRODUCTION FUNCTION VARIABLES FOR A SAMPLE OF 101 FISHING ENTERPRISES, 1963
(Per Vessel in Group)

Group #	PQ (Total Revenue) $	L (Crew Size)	K (Total Assets) $	$\frac{PQ}{L}$ = Value Productivity Per Crewman $	$\frac{K}{L}$ = Assets Per Crewman $	S* (Size of Vessel)
1	45,649.47	4.63	21,406.80	9,859.50	4,623.50	1
2	60,333.00	4.91	19,854.15	12,287.78	4,043.62	1
3	50,989.66	6.67	32,842.52	7,644.63	4,923.92	1
4	206,518.40	12.71	127,229.46	16,248.50	10,101.86	0
5	127,917.92	7.17	59,301.92	17,840.71	8,270.84	0
6	131,713.08	11.17	57,538.24	11,791.68	5,151.14	0
7	24,427.37	4.29	6,320.46	5,694.03	1,473.30	1
8	46,197.13	5.00	20,589.38	9,239.43	4,117.88	1
9	43,394.59	5.33	15,490.02	8,141.57	2,906.20	1
10	191,550.38	12.86	41,331.22	14,895.05	3,213.94	0
11	107,924.13	9.00	30,774.99	11,991.57	3,419.44	0
12	106,919.15	7.40	33,092.74	14,448.53	4,471.99	0
13	144,589.83	11.00	42,737.03	13,144.53	3,885.18	0

* S = 0 large vessels
    1 small vessel
Source: Tables 3 and 4.

still generate more revenue than their smaller counterparts. Thus, factor increases do not account for all of the difference in value productivity between size classifications. Case 3 shows the impact on the regression coefficient of assuming no economies of scale. However, Case 4 illustrates that a significant proportion of labor productivity (also capital productivity) results from scale economies.[21] Capital intensity is still a significant variable in increasing labor productivity. However, the estimated elasticity or parameter of the K/L ratio is reduced from .4966 in Case 3 to .3179 in Case 4 which indicates the economies of scale adjustment.

This section has left a number of problems unsolved. Although significant economies of scale for the fishing enterprise have been identified, the major source of these economies must still be isolated. Large vessels may spend more days at sea per year, be more productive per day, and receive higher prices on the average. At the time of this writing, only limited data were available for judging which of the above factors is more important.[22]

A Note on the Adjustment of Capital
(Total Assets) for Historical Prices

The capital stock used in this analysis is expressed in historical or book value prices. Up to this point, no attempt has been made to express the capital stock in current dollars. The assets of a fishing enterprise in *current dollars* would be the following:

$$TA = CA + \frac{FA}{Pf}$$

where TA; CA; FA; and Pf are total assets, current assets, fixed assets and a price index for fixed assets respectively. FA represent the historical cost of equipment acquired. Although most fishing

---

[21] Scatter diagram 1 indicates that large vessels generally have a higher asset/crew ratio than smaller vessels. Despite this, large vessels are still able to generate more revenue per unit of capital.

[22] The Bureau of Commercial Fisheries provided a special tabulation of the 1964 fishing activity for 98 vessels in our sample. Analysis of the data show that the average large vessel (60 tons or over) engages in fishing (days at sea minus time consumed in transit to and from fishing grounds) 123 days per year. The average small trawler only fishes 74 days per year, although making almost twice as many trips as the larger vessels. Large trawlers greatly outfish the smaller vessels in December through March when the weather is severe. Thus, the 1964 data provide support for the hypothesis that larger vessels are actually utilized more during the year than their smaller counterparts. In addition, large vessels also received a somewhat higher price per pound for their catch in 1964, presumably due to their winter operations.

vessels are old, the turnover rate is very high. This means that the value of older vessels may be expressed in recent prices if they have changed hands in the past few years. For the 101 vessels in our sample, the last date of purchase was obtained from the United States Custom House. When a vessel is sold, the transaction and its date must be registered with the Custom House. Therefore, the asset value on the balance sheet is expressed in a particular year's prices. The average vessel in our sample was purchased approximately 5 years ago even though its average age is over 20 years.

The Maritime Administration's shipbuilding construction cost index was used in conjunction with the last date of purchase information to permit expression of fixed assets for every fishing enterprise in the sample in 1963 dollars.

Number of Years Purchased Prior to 1963, 101 Fishing Vessels in New England

Group	Years	Group	Years
1.	3.1	7.	5.3
2.	3.4	8.	5.1
3.	5.8	9.	7.0
4.	4.4	10.	7.9
5.	2.7	11.	7.7
6.	2.7	12.	6.0
		13.	4.8
All Groups	5.1		

One difficulty with adjustment is that capital improvements may be made in the fixed assets between the purchase date and the current year. Since most vessels in the sample were purchased recently, the results will show only a slight downward bias.

The effect of adjustment of the capital stock for price influence is shown in Table 12. The rate of return is reduced for all groups. However, the rank of groups according to the rate of return is almost unaffected by the price adjustment. Groups 11 and 5 change places after the price adjustment is made. The broad conclusion concerning vessel size and profitability does not seem to be influenced by our adjustment of the capital stock to current dollars.

TABLE 12

**ADJUSTMENT OF ASSETS IN HISTORICAL PRICES
TO 1963 DOLLARS AND COMPARATIVE RATES OF RETURN**

Group #	Rate of Return on Total Assets in Historical Prices: Profits before Taxes ÷ Assets	Rate of Return on Total Assets in 1963 Prices: Profits before Taxes ÷ Assets	Total Assets in 1963 Prices $	Total Assets in Historical Prices $	Difference (Assets in 1963 Prices − Assets in Historical Prices) $	Difference ÷ Assets in Historical Prices
10	13.08%	11.70%	323,358.01	289,318.51	34,039.50	11.8%
11	10.68%	9.15%	215,364.25	184,649.96	30,714.29	16.6%
5	9.82%	9.52%	367,059.59	355,811.51	11,248.08	3.2%
4	3.07%	2.83%	964,555.26	890,606.24	73,949.02	8.3%
13	2.73%	2.01%	348,896.75	256,422.18	92,474.57	36.1%
1	0.36%	0.33%	183,604.23	171,254.40	12,349.83	7.2%
6	− 0.96%	− 0.93%	355,779.42	345,229.43	10,549.99	3.1%
12	− 1.07%	− 0.99%	178,722.71	165,463.68	13,259.03	8.0%
3	− 1.09%	− 1.00%	213,594.94	197,155.11	16,439.83	8.3%
7	− 5.30%	− 4.99%	47,011.05	44,243.25	2,767.80	6.2%
8	− 5.34%	− 4.97%	441,684.87	411,787.66	29,897.21	7.3%
2	− 8.11%	− 7.72%	229,386.76	218,395.62	10,991.14	5.0%
9	−11.07%	−10.46%	98,291.59	92,940.13	5,351.46	5.8%

Source: Federal Reserve Bank of Boston.

COMMENT

ROGER C. VAN TASSEL

Clark University

Dr. Bell has been diligent in his efforts to net an elusive quarry: What is the rate of return upon capital invested in fishing vessels? He has made careful use of the analytical tools and has been able to answer some of the major questions. The stratification of the universe, according to the most likely determinants of earnings, permitted an evaluation of the importance of individual factors.

However, two major limitations exist in the selection of the sample: (1) only corporations could be selected and (2) the sample was limited to Massachusetts. The fact that Massachusetts represents a predominant share of the New England fishing fleet—505 out of 726 vessels—and contains a mixture of vessels paralleling the region reduces the importance of the second limitation. However, the inability to obtain and evaluate data from unincorporated firms operating vessels may be a more serious limitation to the extent the unincorporated vessels represent a significant share of the total and have a considerably different profit record.

Let us look at the central questions discussed in the paper. How profitable is the fishing industry? What factors explain the highly divergent profit records within the industry? The figures in Table 5 show the rate of return on investment in fishing vessels to be significantly less than on investment in manufacturing, mining, or agriculture. This conclusion can be criticized on two grounds. First, as is noted in the paper, the earnings record in the industry is highly volatile and the data used cover only a 2 year period. Second, if the rate of return is computed including interest payments the differential between fishing and the other categories is narrowed. If "officers' compensation" is also included—legitimately I would judge—as a part of the return to the investment base, the New England fishing industry has an average rate of return superior to manufacturing.

However, even if the low figure for the rate of return is correct, the dispersion among firms is so large that at least some segments of the industry earned competitive rates of return. What explains the variability in the rate of return? Dr. Bell suggests some possible answers. The larger vessels tend to show a better rate-of-return.

"The conclusion reached is that approximately nine-tenths of the difference in the rate of return (9.52/10.43) between groups (i.e.; large versus small) is due to the superior income generating power of large vessels."

Why the larger vessels "do better" is important and still uncertain. The most likely explanations do not lie within the usual range of "economies of scale." Larger vessels can average more days per year at sea and tend to receive better prices. These are important advantages. The quality of the captain is also important but much harder to judge. The captain's "pay" is based on a percentage of the ship's catch. Better captains could be expected to gravitate to the larger vessels. An investor in the industry would probably be well advised to build a large vessel, but perhaps should be urged to take great pains in the selection of the captain as well as the design of the vessel.

Dr. Bell has accomplished an interesting research project, has answered some questions, and indicated the direction for further research for those interested in the economics of fishing vessel operations.

THE ECONOMICS

OF THE

SMALL TRAWLER FLEET*

*ANDREAS A. HOLMSEN***

University of Rhode Island

The reason we are meeting at this conference is a common interest in and a common concern for our fishing industry. We all know that the world fish production has increased considerably during the last decade while the U.S. production has been stable; actually it has been stable for the last 3 decades. We know that we are being outfished by the Canadians in the Northwest Atlantic and according to some statistics also have been by-passed by the Russians in the waters outside our coast. I think most of us here also feel that the fishing industry, compared to our other basic industries, generally has been neglected in national policy matters, and is an industry whose interests often have been sacrificed when these have been in conflict with other considerations.

The public interest in our marine-oriented industries seems to be increasing, however, and funds for research in this field are rising. But the bulk of these funds is going into basic research, which, at least at first glance, seems far removed from the immediate problems in the commercial fisheries. Only limited funds are used to help bridge the gap between scientific findings and the problems faced by our commercial fishermen. To do this properly requires a considerable amount of applied research as well as teaching efforts,

*Contribution No. 1177, Agricultural Experiment Station, University of Rhode Island.

**Associate Professor of Food and Resource Economics, University of Rhode Island.

and, whereas little applied research is done, practically no extension work or teaching is being done in this field. This is not only so on the Federal level but also on the State level. If a Fisheries Division in a state has, say, four specialists, chances are that all four are biologists, and that technicians such as vessel specialists and gear specialists are completely lacking. With this unbalanced emphasis it is not a surprise that we often hear fishermen say: "I know that millions of dollars are spent on research in the fisheries field, but please tell me, how has it ever benefitted me?"

The competitive position of our fishing fleet depends on a number of factors such as the relative prices of vessel and gear, the relative availability of capital, the interest rate, the relative supply of competent people for the industry, and the abundance of fish on nearby banks. New England is in a favorable position only when it comes to the closeness of good fishing grounds and the closeness to the market. From the point of view of both labor and capital cost the New England fishing industry is at a disadvantage relative to our foreign competitors. Similarly, the education and training of fishermen has been a thoroughly neglected field, and the law of the 1790's preventing the purchase of foreign vessels for our fishing fleet is an almost unique discrimination against an industry.

Having had the opportunity to get these thoughts off my chest to a captive audience, may I then switch to the topic I was supposed to talk about: the economics of small trawlers. First it should be stressed that no two ports are similar and that findings from one port, even in New England, might not be applicable to another New England port, since factors such as the local labor market and the closeness to fishing grounds and sheltered waters would affect the findings.

Two studies have recently been carried out to determine the return to capital for New England trawlers. At the meeting of the American Fisheries Advisory Committee in October, 1964, Lawrence Van Meir gave a paper describing the cost and returns for large off-shore trawlers in Boston. The study divided the boats into two groups, high earning and low earning vessels and found a return on investment of $13,523 for high earning and $17,590 for low earning vessels. The higher figure according to Mr. Van Meir would give a rate of earning on replacement cost of 2.6 percent a year. Neither total investment figures nor the sample size in the two groups are mentioned in the paper, so the return to capital can not be determined from that paper alone. Further, the depreciation seems to be a rough estimate, and as indicated by the author this could have a significant effect on the return to capital.

Another study conducted this year by Frederick Bell using a stratified sample of 101 Massachusetts trawlers showed a return on total assets of 1.8%, and a return on net worth of 4.8%.[1] According to this study some large trawlers were quite profitable, but the small trawlers had a negative return to capital.

The Department of Food and Resource Economics at the University of Rhode Island is conducting a study of the financing of Rhode Island's trawler fleet, and one aspect of this study in progress is the return to capital invested in small trawlers. This part of the study includes vessels in Point Judith and Newport, Rhode Island and Stonington, Connecticut.

Since our findings differ significantly from the findings in the two studies mentioned and since most of the observations are from Point Judith, it might be best first to point out some of the characteristics of this fishing port.[2] The fleet consists of about 40 draggers, plus some in-shore lobster boats, trap boats, etc., and the fishermen in the port are organized in a co-operative.

The Point Judith Fishermen's Co-operative has about 150 members and is run by a Board of Directors of 7 members. The co-operative operates plants for food fish and now also for trash fish. It has its own unloading facilities, storage, freezers, filleting lines, and it ships food fish by its own trucks primarily to the New York market. The cooperative this year also bought a by-products plant for fishmeal with a capacity of handling 500 tons of fish a day. The co-op has its own ice-making plant and a store open 24 hours a day where gear and supplies can be bought. Other services rendered by the co-op are settlements, group insurance for vessels and a welfare fund. Point Judith has a reasonably good harbor and the fishing fleet is non-unionized.

The data were obtained by personal interviews and pertain to the calendar year 1964, which in Point Judith was not a particularly good, nor a particularly poor year. It was poorer than 1963, but we feel representative of the last 5 years. The prices for trash fish, which in Point Judith is a considerable part of the catch, were lower than in other ports, because the fishmeal plant was not in operation in 1964 and the trash fish had to be unloaded into a

---

[1] Frederick W. Bell, *The Economics of the New England Fishing Industry: The Role of Technological Change and Government Aid*, (Federal Reserve Bank of Boston, Research Report No. 31), p. 62.

[2] Data for the study were collected by Howard Hallberg, graduate student in the Department of Food and Resource Economics.

carrier vessel and shipped to Long Island. Table 1 illustrates the number of records obtained by ports. The sample in the first two ports are representative of these ports as a whole; for Newport, however, there might be a bias in favor of the more profitable vessels.

TABLE 1

NUMBER OF VESSELS IN UNIVERSE AND SAMPLE AND PERCENTAGE DISTRIBUTION BETWEEN PORTS, 1964

	Point Judith	Stonington	Newport	All Ports
Universe	39	14	9	62
Sample	31	10	5	46
Sample size in %	79	71	56	74

Compared to the average size in New England; the trawlers in this study are small. The Point Judith fleet has on the average the smallest vessels, ranging from 35-85 feet in overall length, but they are typically younger and more powerful than in the other two ports. With an average age of 42 years the captains in the Point Judith fleet might be younger than in most other ports, and the port has not so far had much difficulty in attracting young men to the industry.

TABLE 2

SELECTED MEAN CHARACTERISTICS OF SAMPLE VESSELS, 1964

	Point Judith	Stonington	Newport	All Ports
Length, ft.	55	58	61	55
Horse power	206	148	157	188
Age in years	15	23	20	17

TABLE 3

SELECTED CHARACTERISTICS OF CAPTAINS OF SAMPLE VESSELS, 1964

	Point Judith	Stonington	Newport	All Ports
Age of captain	42	45	49	43
Years as captain	14	20	17	16
Years as mate	2	2	3	2
Years as deckhand	4	6	3	4
School grade passed	12	10	9	11

Because of rough weather, particularly in the wintertime, small vessels generally can not put in as many days on the water as the bigger ones. Most of the boats in Point Judith and Stonington, however, are day boats and quick trips out in fairly sheltered waters such as Block Island Sound can be taken even if the weather is rough in other areas, since the steaming to port only takes a short time. The study by Van Meir indicated that the big trawlers in Boston stayed out about 270 days of the year, but fished only about 164 of these. This means that 40% of the time out was not used for fishing, but one would expect, for steaming or riding the weather.

TABLE 4

SELECTED MEASURES OF FISHING EFFORT

	Point Judith	Stonington	Newport	All Ports
No. of days fishing	156	141	149	153
Av. trip length (hrs)	43	58	105	53
Size of crew	3.0	2.9	3.0	3.0

Table 5 shows that the average gross stock for Point Judith trawlers was about $48,000 ranging from about $13,000 to $110,000. What is deducted as trip expense differs somewhat from one vessel to the other and so does the lay system.[3] Some captains deduct electronics as a trip expense, some even deduct food as a trip expense. The most common lay system is the broken 40, but some use the broken 45. In the latter case, however, electronics is not charged as a trip expense.

The average crew share in Point Judith was $8,383 with a range from somewhat above $2,000 to about $14,500 and for "all ports" about $7,700. This is the gross crew share and certain crew expenses such as food, soda, gloves, etc., have to be deducted to determine the net crew share. Exact figures on this are not available, but for Point Judith the crew expense will on an average amount to about $500, which will give the crew a labor income of $7,883.

[3] The lay is the division of the gross stock between boat and crew. With an "even" lay the gross stock is split, while with a "broken" lay certain trip expenses are first deducted. Thus a "broken 40" gives 40 percent to the boat and 60 percent to the crew after trip expenses are deducted.

TABLE 5

GROSS STOCK, TRIP EXPENSES AND AVERAGE CREW SHARE BY PORT, 1964

	Point Judith	Stonington	Newport	All Ports
Gross stock:	$48,046	$38,860	$33,191	$44,434
Trip exp.:				
Fuel, Oil	$3,415	n.a.	$3,859	n.a.
Pumping &				
Lumping	567	n.a.	82	n.a.
Ice	978	n.a.	930	n.a.
Electronics	174	n.a.	102	n.a.
Welfare				
Fund	229			
Other	353	n.a.	48	n.a.
Total Trip				
Expenses	5,716	5,804	5,021	5,659
Gross after				
Trip Exp.	$42,330	$33,056	$28,170	$38,776
Total to Crew	25,148	19,833	16,903	23,097
Average Crew				
Share	$ 8,383	$ 6,839	$ 5,637	$ 7,699

n.a. = not available

TABLE 6

CAPTAIN'S SHARE FOR MANAGEMENT AND NET TO BOAT BY PORT, 1964

	Point Judith	Stonington	Newport	All Ports
Total Boat Share	$17,184	$13,222	$11,268	$15,680
10% of Boat				
Share	1,718	1,322	1,127	1,568
Net to Boat	$15,466	$11,900	$10,141	$14,112

If the owner is not captain of his vessel, the hired captain gets 10% of the boat share in addition to his crew share. This 10% is a return to management, and in this analysis is considered as such whether the vessel is operated with a hired captain or not. The "net to the boat" averaged about $15,500 in Point Judith in 1964 and averaged somewhat above $14,000 for the 3 ports combined. After the boat expenses are deducted from "net to boat" the residual is available for interest and depreciation. The various expense items and their magnitude is shown in Table 7. In the case of Point Judith the boat expenses used up about 2/3 of the "net to boat" while these expenses accounted for a much larger share in the other two ports.

TABLE 7

**BOAT EXPENSES AND AMOUNT AVAILABLE FOR
INTEREST AND DEPRECIATION BY PORTS, 1964**

	Point Judith	Stonington	Newport	All Ports
Net to Boat	$15,466	$11,900	$10,141	$14,112
Expenses:				
Electronics	$ 164	$ 65	$ 0	$ 124
Repairs	3,295	3,198	2,094	3,144
Rope &				
Twine	1,860	2,110	1,440	1,869
Supplies	1,516	2,124	619	1,550
Wharfage	179	6	128	136
Insurance	1,895	1,486	2,293	1,849
Taxes	553	479	500	531
Legal &				
Prof. fees	205	169	55	181
Other				
expenses	536	248	116	427
Total boat exp.	10,203	9,885	7,245	9,811
For interest &				
deprec.	$ 5,263	$ 2,015	$ 2,896	$ 4,301

The most difficult part of a cost-of-production study is how to obtain a realistic depreciation figure. Two problems are involved: first, determining the market value of the vessel and second, selecting the rate of depreciation. Every method will have some weaknesses. The easiest thing would be to use the depreciation figure from the income tax statement. This figure would, however, be too high. If a vessel changes hands often, one can easily, even at a constant price level, get an accumulated depreciation of $100,000 for a vessel which cost $50,000 when new. A vessel in its lifetime might be depreciated to zero a number of times. Another question is to what extent should the price level or the "price index for new vessels" affect the magnitude of depreciation, that is: what will be the replacement cost after x number of years? Some have indicated that it might be advisable to use the original cost of the vessel and a ship building cost index to determine both present value and depreciation of vessels, but someone familiar with our fishing fleet would hardly consider this method.

We approached the problem this way. The owner of the vessel was asked what he considered the market value; this figure was checked with the last appraisal of the vessel by an independent surveyor either for a bank or for an insurance firm. Only on three occasions were there significant differences between the two figures and these differences could be accounted for. The owner was also asked to allocate the total value between hull, engine and electronics. The rate of depreciation was determined by asking the owner how long he thought he would keep the vessel and, assuming a constant price level, what he thought the different components then would be worth (sales value or salvage value). We will be the first to agree that for an individual vessel the rate of depreciation so determined might be off, but these errors are hopefully compensating errors which will be eliminated, or at least considerably reduced, in a large sample. The present market value of the average vessel for each port is presented in Table 8. As expected the "real depreciation" was significantly below the "depreciation for tax purpose," especially so in Point Judith where the vessels are younger than in the two other ports.

TABLE 8

MARKET VALUE AND DEPRECIATION BY PORTS, 1964

	Point Judith	Stonington	Newport	All Ports
Value:				
Hull	$16,184	$13,450	$11,950	$15,128
Engine	6,958	5,070	5,985	6,442
Electronics	5,426	4,480	3,485	5,010
Total vessel	$28,568	$23,000	$21,420	$26,580
"Real" depreciation	1,263	570	1,523	1,141
Depr. for tax purpose	2,813	774	1,923	2,273

After deducting the "real depreciation" from what was left for depreciation and interest we find the return to capital or total assets. The return on total assets in the Point Judith trawler fleet in 1964 was 14% and in Stonington and Newport somewhat above 6%. It should be emphasized again that the sample for Newport may contain an upward bias. The return to capital is in some respects an important figure but to the owner of the vessel the return on his net worth is more important. The average indebtedness in 1964 was 35% of total assets in Point Judith and 26% for "all ports." The interest payments on borrowed capital amounted to only $574 in Point Judith and somewhat above $400 for "all ports." This gives only an average interest rate on borrowed capital of between 5% and 6%. The low interest payments on borrowed capital, however, should not be interpreted to mean that commercial banks' interest rate on fishing vessel mortgages is low, but that most of the capital has been borrowed from the captain's family at no interest or at low interest rates, or that mortgage loans have been made on the fisherman's house rather than on his vessel. The return to net worth of 18.5% in Point Judith indicates that investment in small trawlers can be a profitable investment, since this rate of return is as high as the rate of return on net worth before taxes by all manufacturing corporations.

TABLE 9

RETURN TO CAPITAL BY PORTS, 1964

	Point Judith	Stonington	Newport	All Ports
Left for interest and depreciation	$5,236	$2,016	$2,896	$4,300
Depreciation	1,263	570	1,523	1,141
Return to capital	4,000	1,446	1,373	3,159
% Return to Capital	14.0	6.3	6.4	11.9

TABLE 10

ASSETS, DEBT AND NET WORTH FOR SAMPLE VESSELS BY PORTS, 1964

	Point Judith	Stonington	Newport	All Ports
Total assets	$28,568	$23,000	$21,420	$26,580
Debt	10,067	0	2,387	7,044
Net worth	$18,501	$23,000	$19,033	$19,536
% Net worth	65	100	89	74

TABLE 11

CALCULATION OF AVERAGE RETURN ON NET WORTH BY PORT, 1964

	Point Judith	Stonington	Newport	All Ports
Return on total assets	$4,000	$1,446	$1,373	$3,159
Interest payments	574	0	200	408
Return to net worth	$3,426	$1,446	$1,173	$2,751
% Return to net worth	18.5	6.2	6.2	14.1

Earlier, we indicated that the average crew share for deck hands was $8,383 in Point Judith, $6,839 in Stonington, and $5,637 in Newport (Table 5). With those figures as a starting point it is possible to calculate the earnings of captain/owners. These earnings accrue to the captain/owners by virtue of three specific contributions which they make as workers, as managers, and as investors of capital. The captain's labor income is the crew share minus the crew expenses which is the same income as that of the deck hands. He also has 10% of the boat share as a management income. Assuming that he could invest his money relatively safely at 6% interest, then what he can earn on his money by investing in his own vessel, over and above the 6% opportunity income, can be considered a return on risk and management. The average earnings for a captain in the Point Judith fleet thus were close to $12,000 excluding a "normal" return on his investment.

TABLE 12

**CALCULATION OF AVERAGE IMPUTED EARNINGS OF
OWNER/CAPTAINS BY PORT, 1964**

	Point Judith	Stonington	Newport
Crew share [1]	$8,383	$6,839	$5,637
Estimated crew exp.	500	500	500
Labor income	$ 7,883	$6,339	$5,137
Management income [2]	1,718	1,322	1,127
Return on net worth [3]	3,426	1,446	1,173
−6% opportunity income	1,110	1,380	1,143
Return on risk & management	2,316	66	30
Owner/captain income	$11,917	$7,727	$6,294

[1] **Source:** Table 5
[2] **Source:** Table 6
[3] **Source:** Table 11

The cause and effect relationships have not yet been studied, but by comparing the records of the 12 vessels in Point Judith with the highest rate of return to capital with the 12 with the lowest rate of return some interesting observations can be made. By looking at the characteristics of these two groups, one with a 21.2% return to capital, the other with only 5.0%, the surprising thing is that the average size, strength, and age of the vessel is about the same (except that the high return group has newer engines). The difference is not in the equipment but in the management. It is the difference between a good captain and a not so good captain. The high return group put in 12% more days of fishing and had a 73% higher gross stock than the low return group, and the difference in crew share between the two groups was over $3,000.

Several of the fishermen in Rhode Island are of the opinion that what is needed in the state is not larger trawlers, but a larger fleet of small, powerful trawlers (70-90 feet) and good shore installations. This paper has indicated that small trawlers, on the average, are good investments in Point Judith, giving a return on total assets of 14%. This paper has further indicated that the size, age or value of the vessel has no significant effect on the return to capital, and that the latter primarily is a function of management. This analysis has been presented here to supplement the findings in the two other studies previously mentioned. In conclusion I would like to

TABLE 13

COMPARISON OF VESSELS WITH HIGH & LOW RATE OF RETURN ON CAPITAL

	12 Highest	12 Lowest
% Return on total assets	21.2	5.0
Vessel: Length overall	54.5	54.5
Horsepower	214	203
Age	16	18
Market value total	$29,475	$25,242
Market value hull	15,015	15,308
Market value engine	8,917	4,917
Market value electronics	5,543	5,017
Fishing days	164	146
Gross Stock	$56,914	$32,968
Crew size	3.3	2.8
Individual crew share	$ 9,397	$ 6,159
Boat share	21,089	11,644
Boat expense	11,436	8,154

stress, however, that the return to capital is a coefficient with little or no importance in Point Judith at the present time, since it is a port of owner-operated small trawlers. The coefficient of importance is the return to labor, risk, and management. With respect to this factor larger and newer vessels in Point Judith are far superior to the smaller, older vessels. I will not elaborate at this time; suffice it to say that in Rhode Island a high return to labor, risk, and management is directly related to the size and value of the vessel and the educational level of the captains, and inversely related to both the age of vessel and the age of captain.

COMMENT

RICHARD M. DOHERTY

Metropolitan Area Planning Council

Commonwealth of Massachusetts

One of the underlying assumptions of Professor Holmsen's paper seems to be that the fishing industry of New England is important to the New England economy.

The economic facts of life seem to indicate, however, that the fishing industry is a natural resource industry in the highly-developed manufacturing economy of New England and forms a very small part of that economy.

I agree wholeheartedly with Professor Holmsen's contention that "no two ports are similar" in New England and that findings from one port "might not be applicable to another New England port." As we pointed out in the Boston College Groundfish Study, there is really no such thing as "the New England fishing industry," rather, there is a different industry in each port depending upon the species of fish landed in that port, (for example, haddock in Boston, scallops in New Bedford).[1]

Professor Holmsen points out that depreciation is nothing more than a "rough estimate," and I can only agree with this. Because of the varying depreciation practices among trawler owners, this is the most difficult, if not impossible, factor to quantify in any cost or production study.

There are two significant points regarding the Point Judith Fishery which the Professor points out: (1) the fact of the cooperative arrangement which is very similar to the integration found in Canadian ports and (2) the non-unionization of the fishing fleet in that port. In our studies of the Canadian fishing industry, we found that these were the two major competitive advantages held by the Canadian fishing industry over the New England fishing industry.[2]

Regarding the sample used in this paper, I would ask how was the sample drawn? Was it, in fact, a tabulation of results supplied only by those trawler owners willing to supply information (which

---

[1] E. J. Lynch, R. M. Doherty, and G. P. Draheim, *The Groundfish Industries in New England and Canada,* (United States Fish and Wildlife Service, Circular 121, 1961).

[2] *Ibid.*

was our experience in the Groundfish and Scallop Study)? Or was this a stratified sample from which valid statistical inferences could be made?

The paper, in discussing the results and data drawn from the information supplied, frequently uses the word "average." I would ask if this refers to the mean or median; for instance, "the average crew share" at Point Judith is shown as $8,383, but the range given is between $2,000 and $14,500. This is a rather large spread.

In Table 7 it is significant that repairs and insurance in each of the three ports are a large share of the total boat expenses. I would ask about the relationship of the age of vessels as shown in Table 2 to these costs.

On the whole, I think the paper provides some good insights into the economics of the small trawlers and that the answers to some of the questions posed here and the further detailing of the operations of the industry would provide even further insights.

LABOR, RESOURCE

AND

INDUSTRY PROBLEMS

THE FISHING LABOR FORCE:
SCARCITY OR SURPLUS?

MORTON M. MILLER and VIRGIL J. NORTON

Bureau of Commercial Fisheries

Much attention is now being given to the need for advancing the technology of the United States commercial fisheries. In this age of automation and electronic computers, our harvesting of fishery resources is a curious remnant of another era. Technology has advanced rapidly in domestic and foreign industries. Many of these compete with the U.S. fishing industry for both markets and resources, making the future survival of our commercial fisheries dependent on the adaptation of modern techniques. The peculiarities of commercial fishing, however, dictate a selective approach to new methods backed by a thorough understanding of all the inputs of production—the investment base, the natural resource, and the human resource. This discussion focuses on the latter—the labor input. It attempts to assess how developments in the fishing industry have affected the fishing labor force and to determine how well equipped, in terms of human resources, the fishing industry is to meet its challenges in the present and in the future. Is there or will there be a scarcity or surplus of fishing labor?

An analysis of the fishing labor resource requires, first of all, a determination of its role in the national economy. Like any industry, commercial fishing is part of an interdependent network of economic and social activity. Events, decisions, and trends reverberate throughout the system, giving each part shape and direction. Thus, a key to understanding individual industry phenomena is found in national economic and social developments.

Over the last 15 years, the U.S. work force (including self-employed) has increased by approximately three-quarters of a million persons per year. The national economy has been relatively successful in utilizing its broadened human resource base in that approximately 95 percent of the labor force was employed over the years 1949-1964.[1] Beneath this relatively tranquil surface view of the labor force, however, a new economic and social pattern has taken form—the result of marked shifts in job patterns and incomes.

One of the most striking changes has occurred in agriculture, where mechanization and other technology cut drastically into the number of persons required to operate the Nation's farms, and contributed to a steady population flow from rural to urban centers. In 1949, farm workers comprised nearly 13 percent of the labor force— in 1964 the figure was under 7 percent.[2] For those who stayed to operate the machines, output per man increased sharply. Mechanization, however, drew rather sharp lines between needed and unneeded hands, and the marginal productivity of added labor quickly approached zero—therefore the sharp drop in farm workers.

As in agriculture, the number of persons engaged in commercial fishing as a primary source of earnings has dwindled, especially in recent years. U.S. Census figures show that between 1950 and 1960 the fishing labor force dropped from 77,000 to 41,000.[3] In contrast to agriculture, however, advancing technology in fishing has had only a minor part in influencing this change. To be precise, in most of our fisheries, it is the lag in fish harvesting technology within a dynamic economy that has reduced the number of U.S. fishermen.

Marginal productivity analysis aids in understanding recent developments in the fishing labor force. For the economy as a whole, changes have occurred in factors affecting both the supply of and demand for labor. Increasing marginal productivity of labor, resulting from advances in technology, has enabled the economy to absorb its growing labor force at higher wage levels. That is, the marginal physical product curve has been shifting to the right faster than the

---

[1]Unemployment rates in the civilian labor force during this period ranged between 2.9 and 6.8 percent. The unemployment rate during the latest 5-year period, 1960-64, has averaged 5.8 percent. Source: *Manpower Report of the President,* March 1965, p. 193.

[2]*Ibid.*, p. 202.

[3]U.S. Department of Commerce, *Census of Population,* "Characteristics of the Population," 1960, Vol. I, Part I, p. 527.

supply curve has shifted to the right. Over a 10-year period, for example, the size of the male labor force increased about 5 percent and the average annual wage increased 70 percent—from $2,668 in 1949 to $4,621 in 1959.[4]

Workers are attracted to industries where their marginal revenue product is the greatest. Thus, in order to maintain the labor force in each industry, the marginal productivity in each must keep pace with that in the rest of the economy. However, labor productivity in most fisheries, New England included, has not kept pace. Therefore, the supply of labor to the fishing industry has shifted to the left. The result of a supply curve shifting leftward and a marginal product curve that is constant or shifting to the right at a slower rate, has been a decreased fishing labor force with earnings somewhat higher than before. For example, between 1949 and 1959 average wages of fishermen advanced from a median of $1,575 to $2,395 —about 52 percent—but the number of workers declined sharply.[5]

Comparative unit output indices, as seen in Table 1, give a rough measure of the widening gap between labor productivity in the New England fishing industry and other domestic industries. Considering output per day at sea, both large and medium trawlers landing at Massachusetts ports have made little progress in recent years. Using 1950 as a base year, the 1961 unit output index for large trawlers was up less than 1 percent. At its highest point over the 1950-1961 period, the index stood at 113. It is important to note, the fluctuations in the index are probably due mainly to changes in resource abundance and availability. Medium trawler unit output over the same period was characterized by wide fluctuations, with little growth indicated. In sharp contrast, U.S. agricultural unit output (based on man-hours) was up more than 80 percent between 1950 and 1961, while the non-agricultural industries gained by 30 percent.[6]

Continued failure to keep pace with increasing productivity is certain to magnify the manpower problems of most U.S. fisheries. Labor costs will likely continue to rise and the fishing industry will have to improve its efficiency enough to offset the increased costs. Most of the current fishing labor force will remain employed in the

---

[4] U.S. Department of Commerce, *Census of Population*, "Characteristics of the Population," 1950, Vol. II, Part I, p. 281 and 1960, Vol. I, Part I, p. 554.
[5] *Ibid.*
[6] Man-hour output data for the fisheries are not available. Inasmuch as the best information available indicated little change in sizes of trawler crews during the period cited, output per day at sea should be highly correlated with output per man-hour.

TABLE 1

COMPARATIVE UNIT OUTPUT INDICES:
U.S. INDUSTRIAL OUTPUT PER MAN HOUR VS.
MASSACHUSETTS TRAWLER OUTPUT PER DAY AT SEA

Year	Output per man-hour		Output per day at sea	
	Agric.	Non-agric. industries	Large trawlers	Medium trawlers
1950	100	100	100	100
1951	99	104	113	77
1952	108	107	100	95
1953	120	110	93	85
1954	129	112	108	106
1955	133	118	108	121
1956	136	118	111	142
1957	146	120	100	132
1958	160	121	95	119
1959	159	127	88	109
1960	169	128	98	101
1961	181	130	100	109

Source: **Manpower Report of the President,** March 1965. U.S. Department of the Interior, Bureau of Commercial Fisheries, **Fishery Statistics of the U.S.**

fishing industry, rather than take jobs in other industries. However, as these fishermen retire, there will be few replacements and the number of fishermen will continue to decline.

There is evidence that the differential between fishermen's wages and the average wage for male workers in all industries has increased considerably. In 1949, the average annual wage for all male workers was 69 percent higher than the average fisherman's wage. A decade later, the margin had increased to 93 percent.[7]

The heightened wage disadvantage of fishermen strongly reflects some important long-run changes in the U.S. labor force. In a competitive system, in the long run, industries can be expected to pay identical wages for a given skill in a given locality. Interindustry wage differentials, therefore, are associated with the skill mix, i.e., the ratio of skilled workers to non-skilled. The advance of technology in the United States has brought about a noticeable upgrading of job levels, as industry has demanded larger numbers of skilled people. The greatest relative employment gains have been made in

[7] *Census of Population,* 1950, 1960, *op. cit.*

highly skilled professional and technical categories, where the relatively high marginal product values translate into relatively high earnings. Thus, the increase in average earnings for the total male labor force reflects the increase in the number of higher skilled jobs.

In the commercial fisheries there has been little need to alter the skill mix, as few changes have been made in the techniques of production. Fishermen who are classified as unskilled labor are compensated on the same level as other unskilled labor in the economy. The level of earnings for this unskilled labor group is falling further behind the overall average. As the following table shows, wages in the highly skilled job classes have shown a tendency to cluster more closely about the overall average, while the dispersion increases for the less skilled.

TABLE 2

**RELATIONSHIP BETWEEN MEDIAN ANNUAL EARNINGS OF
TOTAL MALE LABOR FORCE AND SELECTED JOB CLASSIFICATIONS**

Item	1949	1959
	Percent	
Male experienced civilian labor force [1]	100	100
Professional, technical & kindred workers	148	143
Managers, official and proprietors, excluding farm	148	144
Clerical and kindred workers	113	104
Sales workers	113	108
Craftsmen, foremen and kindred workers	117	114
Farmers and farm managers	55	47
Farm laborers	32	23
Operatives	98	93
Laborers, excluding farms	74	64
Fishermen and oystermen [2]	59	52

[1] Median earnings: 1949, $2,668; 1959, $4,621.
[2] Included in classification "Laborers, excluding farms."
Source: U.S. Department of Commerce, **Census of Population**, "Characteristics of the Population," Vol. II, 1950 and Vol. I, 1960.

Short-run factors behind increasing wages, such as minimum wage laws and trade unionism, are not particularly relevant to the fishing industry. For the most part, market forces in the fishing industry, especially on local levels, operate without the restraints known in other industries and are free to set a relatively low wage level. However, the decline in both employment and relative wages in the fishing industry is similar to short-run behavior in a declining industry. In such an instance, the older workers are apparently trapped, while their younger, more mobile confreres escape into expanding industries, where both employment and wages are increasing. Thus, the declining industry must relax hiring standards as relative wage scales are further depressed by the relatively lower marginal productivity.[8]

M. W. Reder, in a study of interindustrial wage differentials summarizes the labor characteristics of a declining industry thusly,

> . . . the conventional short run analysis of a declining industry's relative wage implies that [it] will fall because some workers cannot or will not shift industries, though when they do retire they will not be replaced. As the immobile workers disproportionately represent the older segment of the industry's labor force, it is to be expected that in the short run there will be a decline in the quality of the labor force as well as in employment; this will appear as a change in hiring standards.[9]

Some of the more obvious characteristics of a declining labor force show up in a case study of the Boston offshore trawler fleet. This study, conducted by the authors of this paper, lends strong support to the hypothesis that a declining industry tends to attract or retain the residual in terms of education, training, and skills (a group least likely to adapt to technological change). The average fisherman in this important fleet has more than 30 years experience fishing, and apparently does not possess a skill marketable to other industries. More than two-thirds of this group lists fishing as the only type of job ever held. The engineers of the fleet have worked in other industries to a greater degree than any other single job category, reflecting the wider applicability of their skills. Ordinary fishermen, on the other hand, would likely qualify only for nonskilled jobs in industry—a job category with shrinking opportunities for male workers.

For the most part, crew members are considerably older and not as well educated as the average male U.S. worker. As indicated in Table 3, more than 60 percent of the Boston offshore fishermen

---

[8] "Declining industry," in this instance relates to a decline in terms of employment. In an essay on wage differentials, M. W. Reder applies this definition to an analysis of wage behavior in the laundry industry and in agriculture. See Melvin W. Reder, "Wage Differentials: Theory and Measurement," *Aspects of Labor Economics*—a conference—Princeton University Press, 1962, pp. 257-317.
[9] *Ibid.*, p. 263.

were over 54 years old.[10] In contrast, only 17 percent of the male U.S. labor force was above the 54 year mark, while 63 percent was under 45 years old.[11]

TABLE 3

PERCENTAGE DISTRIBUTION OF U.S. MALE CIVILIAN LABOR FORCE AND BOSTON OFFSHORE TRAWLER LABOR FORCE, BY AGE, YEAR 1964

Age group	Male Labor force[1]	Boston offshore fishermen
	Percent	
Under 25	20	2
25-34	21	10
35-44	22	9
45-54	20	17
55-64	13	41
65 & over	4	21
	100	100

[1] **Source: Manpower Report of the President,** March 1965, p. 195.

A high school education has apparently become commonplace in the United States. In 1964, three-fourths of the male civilian labor force had attended high school, over half had completed four years. Yet, the educational attainment of most fishermen in the Boston offshore fleet ends at grade school. Two-thirds of the fishermen have not attended high school. The comparisons are made in Table 4.

A labor force relatively advanced in average age, but limited in educational development, may be an unsuitable core around which to mobilize a new technology. Recruits able to be trained in new methods are needed.

Traditionally, fishermen for the Boston fleet have been attracted from foreign sources. Thus, it is more than mere coincidence that the median age of the entire foreign-born population of the U.S. (57 in the 1960 Census) is identical to the median age of these Boston fishermen. Most of the Boston offshore labor force originated in the maritime provinces of Canada where active programs are now underway to promote progress in the fisheries, and where serious labor shortages in the fisheries have recently been noted. For example, the following statement appeared in a recent article in the *Canadian Fisherman:*

[10] The median age was 57, the mean 54.
[11] The median fell in the 35-44 year group.

The shortage of skilled manpower has caught the industry unawares. Other industries, in this age of automation, are faced with the same problem but few of them had to come from so far behind or work with personnel having such a generally low level of education. The tremendous growth in new fishing boats and new plants in the last few years has turned the spotlight on this glaring weakness which one fishing company executive has termed: 'The greatest single problem facing the industry today. If we don't solve it, we won't be in business ten years from now.'[12]

TABLE 4

EDUCATION ACHIEVEMENTS OF THE U.S. MALE CIVILIAN LABOR FORCE AND OF BOSTON OFFSHORE TRAWLER LABOR FORCE, 1964

	Male civilian labor force [1]	Boston offshore fishermen
	Percent:	
Attended college	23	6 [2]
Did **not** attend college	77	94
With high school diploma	54	19
Without high school diploma	46	81
With some high school attendance	73	37
With **no** high school	27	63 [3]

[1] **Source: Manpower Report of the President,** March 1965, p. 225.
[2] Includes 2 percent with post-high school training other than college.
[3] Includes 4 percent with no formal education.

Canada, in fact, is seeking to encourage immigration of trained fishermen from other nations.[13] A reduced rate of immigration of fishermen from Canada will be felt especially in the ranks of qualified skippers, mates, and engineers. In the Boston offshore fleet, 83 percent of the captains and mates, and 56 percent of the engineers are from Newfoundland or Nova Scotia.[14]

---

[12]Allan T. Muir, "Crashing the Manpower Shortage Barrier," *Canadian Fisherman,* Nov. 1965, p. 23.

[13]See "Shortage of Fishermen," *The Atlantic Fishermen and Shipping Review,* Aug., 1965, p. 12.

[14]Sixty-five percent of captains and mates are from Newfoundland, while 45 percent of engineers are from Nova Scotia.

The type of skill that will be needed in future fishing operations needs careful consideration, just as the type of technology to which it will be applied. It may be that relatively short training periods will produce an adequately competent fisherman. The skill requirements for a job as captain, mate, or engineer, however, are well above that of the ordinary deckhand, even under present technology. This skill is gained through training and long experience. Most candidates for the job of captain, mate, or engineer develop from the ranks of fishermen.

If the conditions in the Boston offshore trawler fleet are representative, the supplies of qualified captains, mates, and engineers promise to become exceedingly tight. The average captain in the Boston fleet in 1964 was 56 years old, while the average age of mates and engineers was 59. This would indicate a work-life expectancy for the present complement of about 10 years. With the average age of ordinary fishermen equally high, the logical pool from which to draw the higher skills is evaporating. Less than one-fourth of the deckhands in the Boston fleet—about 105 men—are under 45. The present fleet operates with a total of 112 captains, mates, and engineers. Thus, in the future, if these highly skilled jobs must be filled from within the fleet, the requirements apparently exceed the number available. This observation is given more weight by the fact that most ordinary fishermen apparently do not qualify for a higher skilled position during their work life. Only one out of ten of the fishermen (deckhands) is presently licensed to serve as a captain, mate, or engineer. Although licenses are not mandatory for all vessels, the low number of license holders indicates a relative scarcity of qualified hands.

Evidence produced in the Boston study warns that the area faces serious shortages in commercial fishing manpower in both skills and numbers. Labor developments on a national scale also indicate a probability of labor scarcities in other fisheries, especially in skills. With the importation of foreign fishing skills at a virtual standstill, the fishing industry is almost completely dependent on the domestic labor market, where four sources of supply are available:

1. other fisheries,
2. other industries,
3. the hard core unemployed, and
4. new entrants into the labor force.

Before any of these sources can be tapped, however, earnings in the fisheries must be comparable to earnings in other industries.

Even if fishing wages were to rise to comparable levels, the attraction of labor would still be difficult. Reasons for this are listed in the following evaluation of the aforementioned sources of fishing labor supply:

1. *Other fisheries.* The desirability of hiring experienced workers cannot be discounted. However, if the "declining industry" hypothesis holds, the pool of desirable workers in other fisheries is apt to be drying. Another factor—more sociological than economic—however, makes this source even less promising. Where geographical shifts are concerned, the attitudes of fishermen likely parallel those of workers in other occupations who are thought to be "sufficiently attached to their home communities so that they have little interest in jobs elsewhere, even at considerably higher wages."[15] Over 60 percent of the fishermen who worked aboard the offshore Boston trawlers in 1964, indicated that they have never worked as fishermen outside the New England region. Nearly 40 percent of these fishermen have spent an entire fishing career working out of Boston.

2. *Other industries.* The classic immobility of labor in the short run would also seem to rule out other industries as a likely source of new fishermen. (We are assuming here movements on the same occupational level.) L. G. Reynolds states:

> Most workers already have jobs with which they are reasonably well satisfied. These people do not behave like participants in a market; they are members of an organization with which they hope and expect to remain indefinitely. There is an economic basis for this since both income and security tend to be increasing functions of length of service with a particular firm.[16]

3. *The hard core unemployed.* It is likely that a large portion of this group is made up of less employable types, such as the very old, or those with relatively little trade skill or little capacity to learn new skills. On the other hand, the ranks of unemployed in some geographical areas of limited job opportunities likely would yield some promising candidates for fishery jobs. Therefore, efforts to recruit from this group may be desirable.

4. *New labor force entrants.* For the purpose of this analysis, this term can be loosely defined as that portion of the male civilian labor force aged 14 to 19. In 1964, there were nearly 4 million persons in this group, 15 percent of whom were unemployed.[17] This is

[15] Lloyd G. Reynolds, "A Survey of Contemporary Economics," *Economics of Labor,* Homewood, Illinois, 1948, Richard D. Irwin, Inc., p. 273.
[16] *Ibid.,* p. 274.
[17] *Manpower Report of the President,* March 1965, p. 195 and p. 205.

a group that is seeking a foothold in the labor market. It is a group especially vulnerable to layoffs, and for which unemployment rates are high and job changes frequent. It is also a group which seeks direction and training and is relatively well equipped to utilize training. This group, therefore, appears to be the most logical from which to recruit new fishermen.

The likelihood of attracting and holding a suitable fishing work force depends on whether or not conditions in the fishing industry improve. Earning possibilities must be brought to levels more comparable to national norms. In order to accomplish this, production efficiency must be improved through the adoption of advanced technology. Modernized fishing operations would tend to upgrade the skill mix requirement in the industry. This would upgrade the quality of the labor force, increase its marginal value productivity, and thus its earnings.

Because factors other than wage earnings influence workers in job decisions, there is also a need to update non-wage benefits, such as paid vacations, and to improve the working environment which for offshore fishermen, in particular, includes vessel living and safety conditions. Although these changes would entail a cost to vessel owners, in the long run the cost of *not* making these changes might be even greater.

This paper has examined changes in the fishing labor force resulting from the changing relationship between the fishing industry and the rest of the economy. Lagging technology has been a prime factor behind the lower productivity of commercial fishermen. Technological improvements are needed in commercial fishing in order to meet conditions for attracting an efficient labor force. These improvements, however, call for higher skills in the fishing force—skills attainable through training. It seems clear that there is a scarcity of fishermen, but it is a scarcity related more to skills than to numbers. In the future, improved technology would likely intensify this scarcity unless, at the present, measures are taken to develop these skills.

This thought has been summarized by C. C. Killingsworth in an essay on automation and manpower. He wrote:

> More investment in plant and equipment, without very large increases in our investment in human beings, seems certain to enlarge the surplus of under-developed manpower and to create a shortage of the

highly developed manpower needed to design, install and [operate] modern production facilities.[18]

COMMENT

JAMES D. ACKERT

Atlantic Fishermen's Union

There is no scarcity of fishermen for the better earning boats ($7,000 to $12,000), however, there is a scarcity of fishermen for the boats whose earnings are around $4,000 to $6,000.

Unfortunately, we have approximately 50% of our fleet that is in the lower income bracket. Also, because of the poor living quarters and the heavy breakdown factor, a man does not stay aboard one of these vessels for long. The turnover factor of the crew is very high because when a place on a higher earning vessel becomes available he will leave.

On completion of every one of our training programs it has been necessary to ship these new men aboard some of the older vessels; and, the net result is, after one or two trips, we find we have lost 50% of the trainees.

It is interesting to note that with the arrival of four (4) new boats in our fleet, approximately twenty of our forty year old men are back fishing. If new vessels were built many more men of this age group would come back to fishing.

Also, in regard to fringe benefits, such as, health welfare and pension funds, it has only been in the last two years that we have been able to offer these benefits to our men. The owners must realize that it is necessary to match any benefits that other industries offer to their employees.

In closing I must stress that there is no shortage of fishermen at this time, if they are given decent vessels to sail on and a decent and good take-home pay.

---

[18]Charles C. Killingsworth, "Automation, Jobs and Manpower," *Labor and the National Economy*. New York, 1965, W. W. Norton & Co., Inc., p. 134.

THE OFFSHORE RESOURCES
OF THE NORTHWEST ATLANTIC

HERBERT W. GRAHAM

Bureau of Commercial Fisheries

The Northwest Atlantic is one of the richest fishing areas of the world. Favorable hydrographic conditions over broad expanses of the continental shelf result in high organic production which supports an abundance of fish that have been in great demand by man for hundreds of years. The landings from the Northwest Atlantic have been an appreciable part of world marine fish production since the discovery of America.

Reliable statistics are not available for the early years, but we know that in 1930 the catch of cod alone in the Northwest Atlantic, amounting to 56,600 metric tons, was over 5% of the entire world production of all fish, freshwater and marine.[1] By 1954, when world landings of marine fishes had increased to 23 million metric tons, the Northwest Atlantic catch amounted to 1.8 million metric tons or 8%; and in 1964 the catch of 2.9 million metric tons from the Northwest Atlantic was still 7% of the 44 million metric ton world total of marine fishes.[2]

In the early days of the Northwest Atlantic fishery, cod accounted for most of the catch. Today, it is still the leading species in terms of pounds landed, but many other species of groundfish, pelagic fish, and shellfish are taken as well. The present composition of the catch is shown in Table 1.[3]

---

[1] *Statistical Bulletin,* Vol. 2 (1952), International Commission for the Northwest Atlantic Fisheries. Also see George Borsstrom, *Fish as Food.* Vol. 1 (Academic Press, 1961).

[2] *Statistical Bulletin,* Vol. 14 (1964), International Commission for the Northwest Atlantic Fisheries (In Print). Also see *Year Book of Fishery Statistics,* Vol. 17 (1964), Food and Agricultural Organization of the United Nations.

[3] All statistics presented in tables and charts in this paper are from the Bureau of Commercial Fisheries and *Statistical Bulletin,* ICNAF.

TABLE 1

**LANDINGS FROM THE NORTHWEST ATLANTIC IN 1964,
BY SPECIES (THOUSANDS OF METRIC TONS, LIVE WEIGHT)**

Species	Landings	Percent
Cod	1,402	47.5
Silver hake	302	10.2
Herring	302	10.2
Redfish	213	7.2
Flounder	148	5.0
Haddock	142	4.8
Sea scallop	117	4.0
Pollock	44	1.5
Red hake	32	1.1
Lobster	30	1.0
Argentines	18	0.6
Mackerel	13	0.4
Squid	11	0.4
Other species	177	6.1
Total	2,951	100.0

The fishery of the Northwest Atlantic has been international since its inception at the time of the discovery of America, and has become even more so during the last decade. Portuguese and French cod fishermen of the North Atlantic extended their activities to the Grand Bank of Newfoundland before the continent was settled. Others followed until today 11 European countries and Japan fish side by side with Canadian and U.S. fishermen. Table 2 presents the distribution of the catch by country for 1964. For a long time the intensive fishery was concentrated on the Grand Bank, but today European fleets are working as far south as Georges Bank off Cape Cod and even farther south along the Atlantic Coast.

This increased fishing effort by European nations has increased total production from the area. U.S. production, on the contrary, has declined somewhat and the U.S. percentage of the total has dropped from more than 28 to about 13 in the last 6 years (Figure 1).

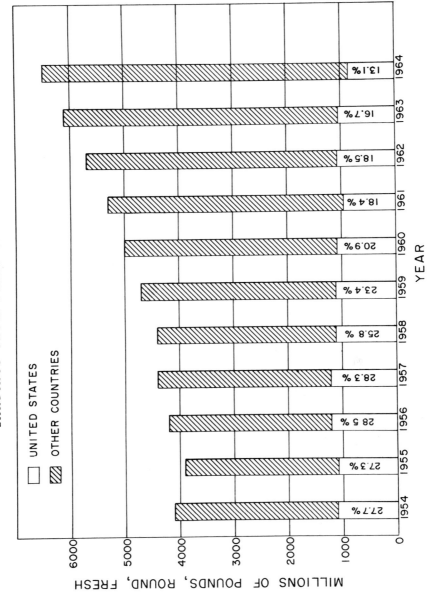

LANDINGS FROM ICNAF CONVENTION AREA

TABLE 2

**LANDINGS FROM THE NORTHWEST ATLANTIC IN 1964, BY COUNTRY
(THOUSANDS OF METRIC TONS, LIVE WEIGHT)**

Country	Landings	Percent
Canada	827	28.0
USSR	617	20.9
USA	388	13.1
Spain	231	7.8
Portugal	210	7.1
France	160	5.4
Germany	149	5.1
Denmark	127	4.3
Nonmembers of ICNAF	95	3.2
UK	52	1.8
Norway	50	1.7
Poland	37	1.3
Iceland	8	0.3
Italy	0	0.9
Total	2,951	100.0

Realizing the increasing intensity of fishing and fearing that overexploitation might operate to the detriment of the catches, the countries fishing in the Northwest Atlantic in 1949 signed a convention which resulted in the implementation of the International Commission for the Northwest Atlantic Fisheries (ICNAF). This Commission held its first annual meeting in 1951. The purpose of the Commission is to investigate, protect, and conserve the fisheries of the Northwest Atlantic Ocean "in order to make possible the maintenance of a maximum sustained catch from those fisheries."[4]

Estimation of the resource base in the Convention Area, which extends from Greenland to Rhode Island (Figure 2) is, of course, one of the prime responsibilities of ICNAF scientists. One of the first activities of the Commission was the compilation and publication of detailed statistics on the catch and on the activities of the various fishing fleets in the area. We now have available on an annual basis information on catch and effort which can be used for

[4] *Report of the First Annual Meeting.* Report No. 1, International Commission for the Northwest Atlantic Fisheries (1951).

Figure 2

CONVENTION AREA OF THE INTERNATIONAL COMMISSION OF THE NORTHWEST ATLANTIC FISHERIES, SHOWING THE FIVE SUBAREAS

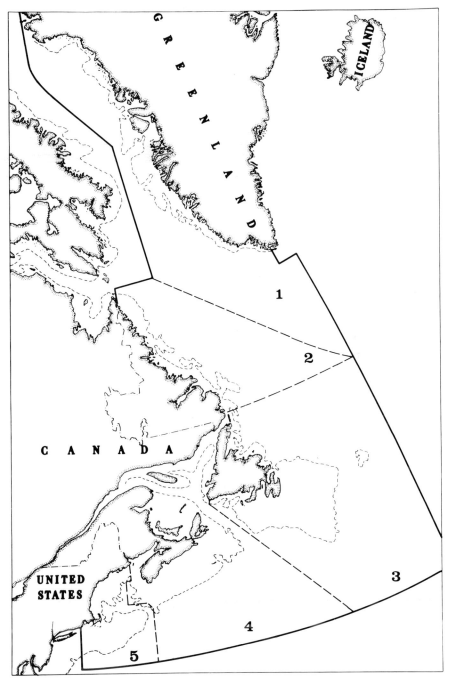

recommending regulations. Early in its history, the Commission imposed minimum-mesh regulations in certain subareas and it is now considering other management measures. Central to all these considerations is the size of the resource and the tonnage of fish which we can hope to take from the area on a sustained basis.

Since many species are involved in the fishery and different stocks of each species occupy different areas, the estimation of sustained yields is complicated. ICNAF scientists have been studying this problem for many years, however, and have arrived at some rather general conclusions. They have some broad estimates of where we are at present on the yield-effort curve, even though they have not, as a rule, indicated a sustainable yield figure for particular stocks. One of the difficulties, of course, is the great variation in recruitment which occurs in most stocks and the fact that we do not understand what relationship, if any, stock size has to recruitment.[5] The general conclusion, however, is that fishing effort in the Convention Area has reached a point where many stocks are now producing at the maximum level and that further effort would not increase the sustainable yield, but might, in fact, result in lower long-term yields. These conclusions relate primarily to stocks which have been traditionally fished for many years, such as the Grand Bank cod and the Georges Bank haddock. If we consider all stocks, including some that are underfished, such as the red hake, it is probable that present total landings are about 20% under total sustainable tonnage.

To present a general idea of the magnitude of each important stock of fish in the offshore waters of the Northwest Atlantic, a series of landing statistics are shown in Tables 3 to 13. The statistics, broken down by ICNAF Subarea (see Figure 2), present values for all countries combined and for the United States alone. Under the column "high year" is given the tonnage for the highest year on record. The figures for the "low year" are for the lowest year since ICNAF statistics became available in 1951. The average for 1952-64 and the figure for 1964 are useful in appraising present exploitation in relation to sustainable yield.

The figures on sustainable yield are given only for cod, haddock, redfish, yellowtail flounder, silver hake, red hake, herring and sea scallops. Adequate information is lacking on which to base estimates of yields for the other species. The sustainable yield figures presented here were arrived at by a study of growth rates, mortality

[5] Recruitment is that increment to the fish population resulting from increased survival over a period of time.

rates, and a time series of effort-catch per effort relations; they assume average, long-term recruitment. Admittedly, they are estimates and subject to change, but they are based on scientific judgment. It must be stressed that because long-term, average recruitment is assumed, the sustainable yield figures are long-term averages in themselves. Recruitment is notoriously variable. When recruitment is high, stock size increases and the yield for a few years may be much higher than the long-term sustainable yield. Indeed, in an ideal management program the yield should be allowed to increase under these circumstances. Conversely, when recruitment is low and the stock size diminishes, yields should be kept at a lower level.

Cod

Cod, the old standby of the Northwest Atlantic fisheries, has in the last few years provided greater tonnage than ever before, although the U.S. catch has not increased and has been below the levels of former decades (Figure 3). It is probable that the species is being fished too intensively on the Grand Bank (Subarea 3) although maximum yields are probably not being reached south of that area except on Georges Bank (Subarea 5), where annual landings in recent years have been near the estimated maximum sustainable yield (Table 3).

TABLE 3

COD STATISTICS, ICNAF CONVENTION AREA
(Thousands of Metric Tons, Live Weight)

| Locality of fishing | Landings | | | | Estimated sustainable yield |
	High year	Low year	Average 1952-1964	1964	
Subarea 3					
All countries	581.4 (1964)	328.0 (1952)	423.6	581.4	400
U.S.	23.8 (1895)	0 [1]	0.2	0	—
Subarea 4					
All countries	229.0 (1964)	132.0 (1952)	192.2	229.0	250
U.S.	43.9 (1945)	1.3 (1963)	2.4	1.4	—
Subarea 5					
All countries	63.7 (1895)	11.2 (1953)	17.2	28.4	25
U.S.	63.7 (1895)	11.2 (1953)	14.7	15.6	—

[1] During World War II.

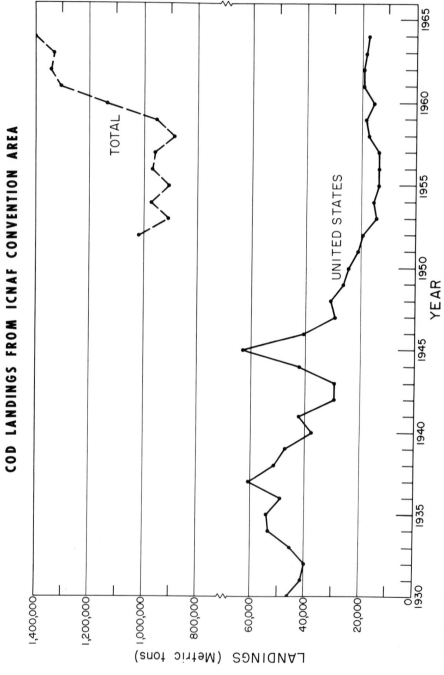

Figure 3

COD LANDINGS FROM ICNAF CONVENTION AREA

Silver Hake (Whiting)

Until 1962 silver hake was taken only by the United States. In that year the USSR started intensive exploitation and the catch skyrocketed (Figure 4). The United States lands this species both for food and for industrial purposes. The United States has confined its silver hake fishing to Georges Bank, the Gulf of Maine, and southern New England banks (Subarea 5) but the USSR has fished the Nova Scotian Banks (Subarea 4) as well. The species does not occur in commercial quantities north of this Subarea.

TABLE 4

SILVER HAKE STATISTICS, ICNAF CONVENTION AREA
(Thousands of Metric Tons, Live Weight) [1]

Locality of fishing	Landings		Average 1952-1964	1964	Estimated sustainable yield
	High year	Low year			
Subarea 4					
All countries	123.0 (1963)	—	18.6	81.1	100?
U.S.	0	0	0	0	—
Subarea 5					
All countries	220.4 (1964)	45.8 (1961)	82.5	220.4	200?
U.S.	78.7 (1957)	45.8 (1961)	58.1	53.1	—

[1] Includes industrial landings.

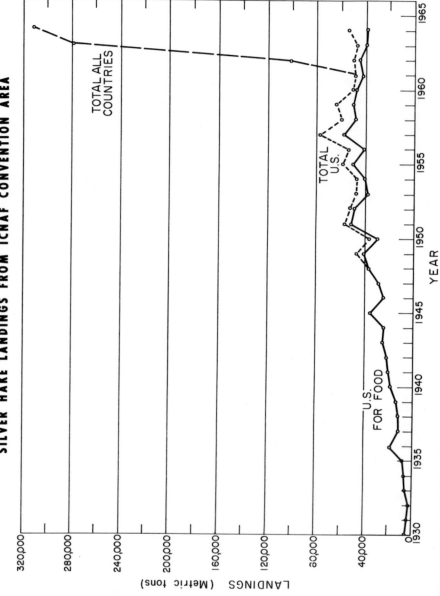

Figure 4

SILVER HAKE LANDINGS FROM ICNAF CONVENTION AREA

Herring

Herring is taken in large quantities by Canada, the USSR, and the United States (Figure 5 and Table 5). Canada and the United States fish primarily the inshore stocks of immature fish for canning as sardines but the USSR fishes offshore stocks of mature fish. USSR fishing started in 1962. We do not have adequate information for estimating long-term sustainable yields, but there are indications that the high landings in 1962 and subsequent years are near the maximum sustainable yield.

TABLE 5

HERRING STATISTICS, ICNAF CONVENTION AREA
(Thousands of Metric Tons, Live Weight)

Locality of fishing	Landings				Estimated sustainable yield
	High year	Low year	Average 1952-1964	1964	
Subarea 3					
All countries	10.8 (1958)	3.3 (1964)	5.8	3.3	10?
U.S.	0	0	0	0	—
Subarea 4					
All countries	139.5 (1964)	77.9 (1956)	97.8	139.5	100-150?
U.S.	0	0	0	0	—
Subarea 5					
All countries	223.3 (1962)	47.6 (1959)	92.6	159.4	120-200?
U.S.	71.8 (1962)	28.0 (1964)	58.3	28.0	—

Figure 5

HERRING LANDINGS FROM ICNAF CONVENTION AREA

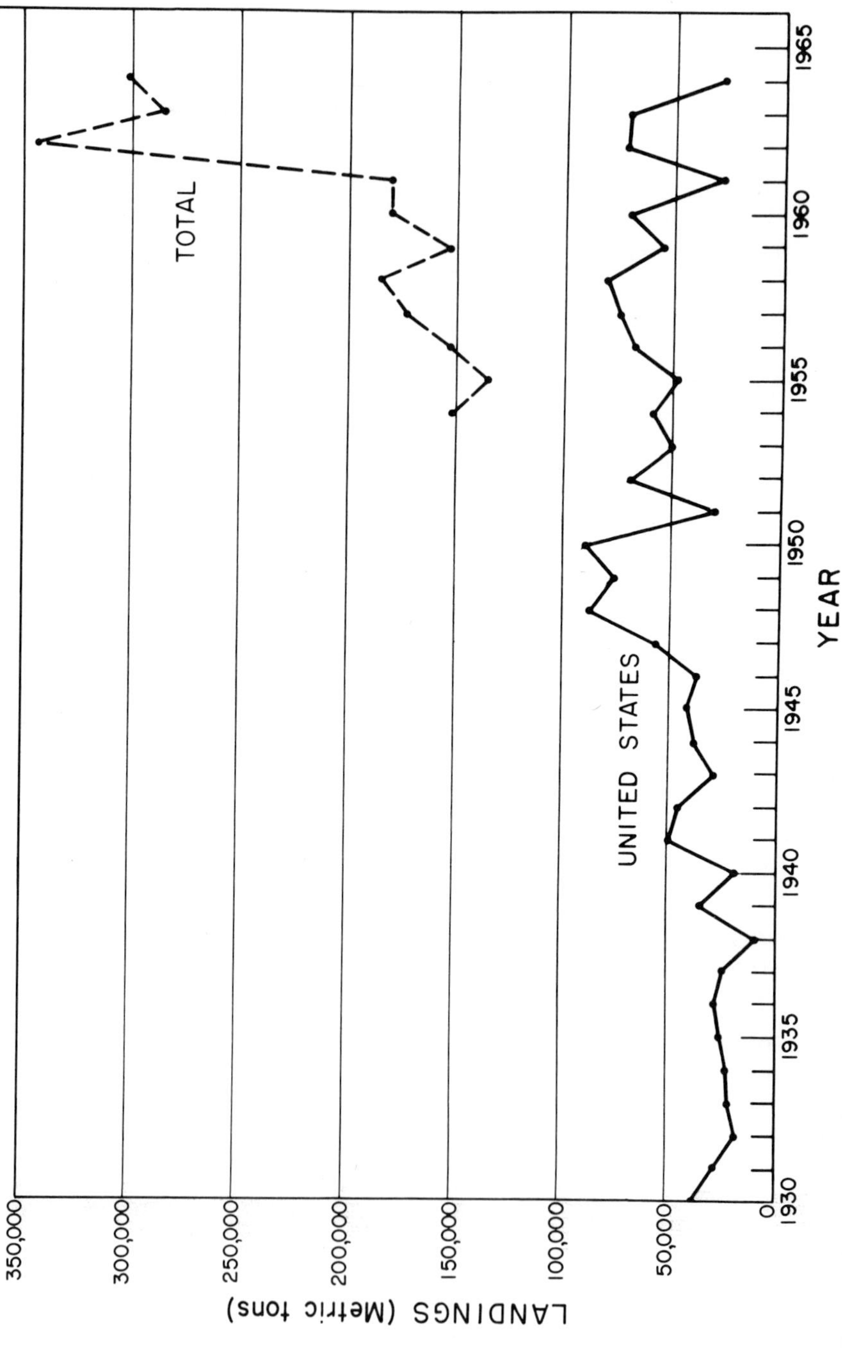

Redfish (Ocean Perch)

The U.S. redfish fishery was developed in the 1930's and reached a peak in 1951, after which it declined (Figure 6). Canadian and European exploitation, started in the 1950's, resulted in a tremendous increase of production for a few years but the catch now appears to be stabilizing at a lower level. Economic factors rather than abundance appear to be limiting the catch at the present time as the estimated maximum sustainable yields for all subareas are higher than the yields being obtained at present levels of exploitation (Table 6).

TABLE 6

REDFISH STATISTICS, ICNAF CONVENTION AREA
(Thousands of Metric Tons, Live Weight)

Locality of fishing	Landings				Estimated sustainable yield
	High year	Low year	Average 1952-1964	1964	
Subarea 3					
All countries	246.1 (1959)	17.6 (1955)	80.0	94.6	75-150?
U.S. (all from 3 NOP (So. Grand Banks)	33.1 (1953)	4.7 (1959)	16.7	4.7	—
Subarea 4					
All countries	76.7 (1949)	28.6 (1953)	49.2	52.6	65-70
U.S.	76.7 (1949)	19.6 (1953)	33.3	27.9	—
4RST (Gulf of St. Lawrence)					
All countries	49.8 (1955)	6.6 (1962)	24.2	29.8	(25?) [1]
U.S.	34.6 (1955)	0 (1962)	10.4	12.2	—
4VWX (Nova Scotian Banks)					
All countries	76.7 (1949)	9.7 (1955)	23.9	22.8	(45?)
U.S.	76.7 (1949)	9.4 (1955)	20.3	15.7	—
Subarea 5					
All countries	59.8 (1941)	8.3 (1964)	14.4	8.3	15-20?
U.S.	59.8 (1941)	7.8 (1964)	14.0	7.8	—

[1] Values in parentheses not additive.

Figure 6

REDFISH LANDINGS FROM ICNAF CONVENTION AREA

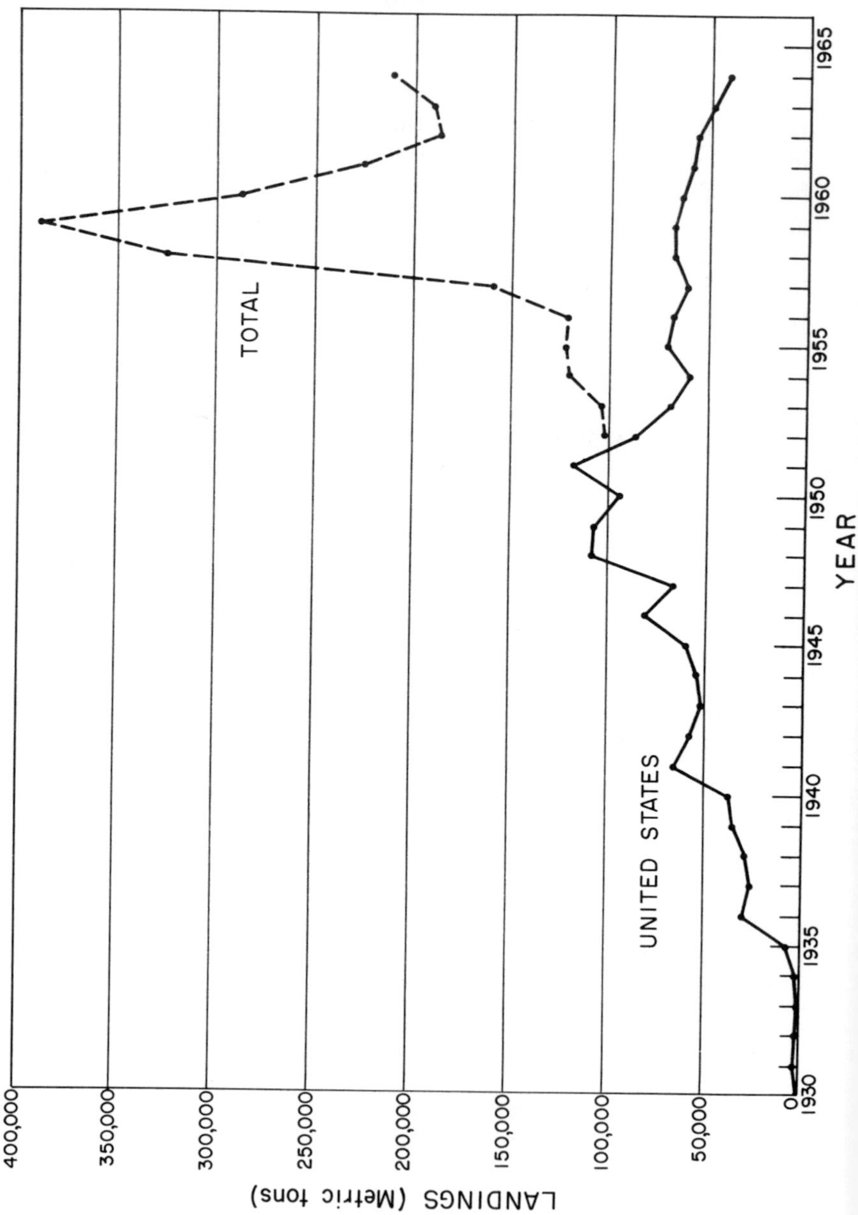

Flounders

The flounder of greatest interest to the United States is the yellowtail (Figure 7). Annual fluctuations in landings result primarily from fluctuations in abundance due to varying recruitment. The value of 25,000 metric tons for the estimated average annual yield in Subarea 5 is less than the amount landed in 1964 (Table 7). This value does not mean the stock is being overfished. Landings have been high in recent years due to unusually good recruitment.

Flounders other than yellowtail are taken in some quantity in all subareas (Table 8), but we have no basis for making estimates of yield for these species.

TABLE 7

YELLOWTAIL FLOUNDER STATISTICS, ICNAF CONVENTION AREA
(Thousands of Metric Tons, Live Weight)

Locality of fishing	Landings				Estimated sustainable yield
	High year	Low year	Average 1952-1964	1964	
Subarea 4					
All countries	5.4 (1964)	0.0 (1956)	1.8	5.4	10?
U.S.	0	0	0	0	—
Subarea 5					
All countries	36.6 (1964)	5.2 (1954)	15.6	36.6	25
U.S.	36.3 (1964)	5.2 (1954)	15.1	36.3	—

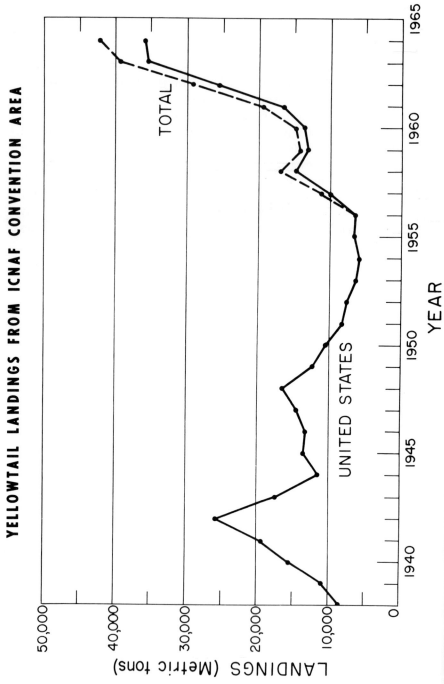

Figure 7

YELLOWTAIL LANDINGS FROM ICNAF CONVENTION AREA

TABLE 8

STATISTICS FOR FLOUNDER, OTHER THAN YELLOWTAIL, ICNAF CONVENTION AREA
(Thousands of Metric Tons, Live Weight)

Locality of fishing	Landings				Estimated sustainable yield [1]
	High year	Low year	Average 1952-1964	1964	
Subarea 3					
All countries	48.5 (1964)	11.4 (1954)	26.9	48.5	?
U.S.	0	0	0	0	—
Subarea 4					
All countries	33.4 (1963)	15.2 (1957)	21.7	28.4	?
U.S.	3.2 (1954)	0.2 (1960)	0.8	0.2	—
Subarea 5					
All countries	20.9 (1964)	11.1 (1958)	12.2	20.9	?
U.S.	20.8 (1950)	9.7 (1962)	11.5	16.8	—

[1] Probably not fully exploited.

Haddock

Haddock landings from the Convention Area have fluctuated widely due to effects of fluctuations in recruitment on the abundance (Figure 8). These wide changes are particularly common in the Grand Bank area, which is the northern limit of the haddock's geographic range and where a good year class occurs only occasionally. United States landings, primarily from Georges Bank (Subarea 5) and Browns Bank (southern part of Subarea 4), have been generally lower in the last few years than previously.

The Georges Bank haddock stock has been studied intensively for many years so that the estimates of maximum sustainable yield are probably better documented than those for any other ICNAF stock. It should be noted that the estimated maximum value of 50,000 metric tons has been exceeded during the past few years (Table 9). Landings from Subarea 4 are also now near the maximum sustainable yield; landings from Subarea 3 have been low recently due to poor recruitment.

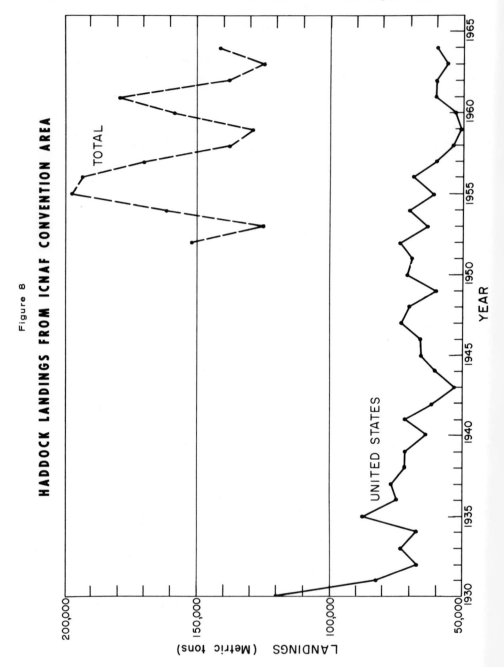

Figure 8

HADDOCK LANDINGS FROM ICNAF CONVENTION AREA

TABLE 9

HADDOCK STATISTICS, ICNAF CONVENTION AREA
(Thousands of Metric Tons, Live Weight)

Locality of fishing	Landings				Estimated sustainable yield
	High year	Low year	Average 1952-1964	1964	
Subarea 3					
All countries	104.5 (1955)	12.4 (1964)	48.1	12.4	50.0
U.S.	0	0	0	0	—
Subarea 4					
All countries	60.0 (1964)	43.1 (1955)	49.3	60.0	60.0
U.S.	50.0 (1935)	6.4 (1962)	12.4	8.4	—
4X (Browns Bank)					
All countries	36.0 (1964)	7.9 (1953)	19.7	36.0	(20.0) [1]
U.S.	15.0 (1931)	5.4 (1959)	8.3	8.5	—
4VW (Eastern Nova Scotian Banks)					
All countries	34.9 (1959)	13.0 (1953)	24.6	22.8	(35.0)
U.S.	9.3 (1948)	0.0 (1964)	2.3	0	—
Subarea 5					
All countries	120.0 (1929)	40.7 (1959)	52.5	69.5	50.0
U.S.	120.0 (1929)	40.5 (1959)	49.6	51.9	—

[1] Values in parentheses not additive.

Sea Scallops

The sea scallop fishery has expanded rapidly since the 1930's (Figure 9). An unusually large year class recruited in 1959 supported the fishery for several years. The expansion of the Canadian fleet of scallop vessels at that time raised the total ICNAF landings well above that of the United States from that year on. Most of the sea scallops come from Subarea 5 (Table 10). Recruitment of scallops is so highly variable that fluctuations in landings can be expected under conditions of heavy fishing pressure but the long-term maximum sustainable yield is probably about 100,000 metric tons live weight (12,000 metric tons of meats) for Georges Bank and 5,000 metric tons live weight (600 metric tons of meat) for Subarea 4.

Figure 9

SCALLOP LANDINGS FROM ICNAF CONVENTION AREA

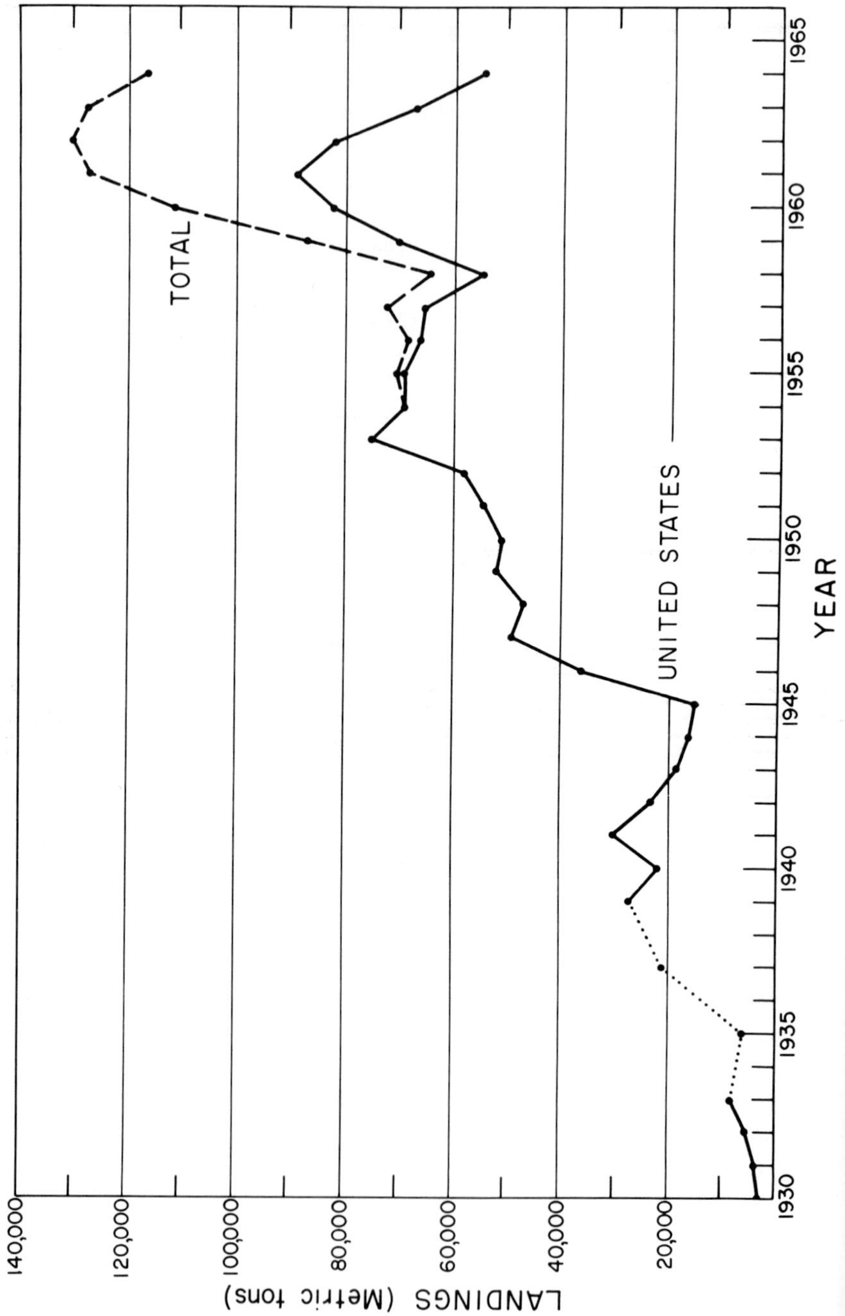

TABLE 10

SEA SCALLOP STATISTICS, ICNAF CONVENTION AREA
(Thousands of Metric Tons, Live Weight)
(Meat Weights in Parentheses)

Locality of fishing	Landings				Estimated sustainable yield
	High year	Low year	Average 1952-1964	1964	
Subarea 4					
All countries	11.5 (1963)	1.6 (1960)	5.4	10.7	5?
	(1.4)	(0.2)	(0.7)	(1.3)	(0.6)[1]
U.S.	0	0	0	0	—
Subarea 5					
All countries	129.0 (1962)	61.5 (1955)	92.5	103.2	100
	(15.5)	(7.4)	(11.1)	(12.4)	(12)
U.S.	89.8 (1961)	44.8 (1958)	64.4	54.1)	—
	(10.8)	(5.4)	(7.7)	(6.5)	

[1] Values in parentheses not additive.

Red Hake

Red hake occurs in commercial concentrations only in the southern part of the Convention Area and was taken only by the United States until 1963, when the USSR started fishing it (Figure 10). Most of the red hake landed by the United States is landed for industrial purposes; a small quantity is for food (Table 11). This species is fairly abundant in the southern part of the Convention Area and is at present underexploited. The long-term maximum sustainable yield is estimated to be 100,000 metric tons.

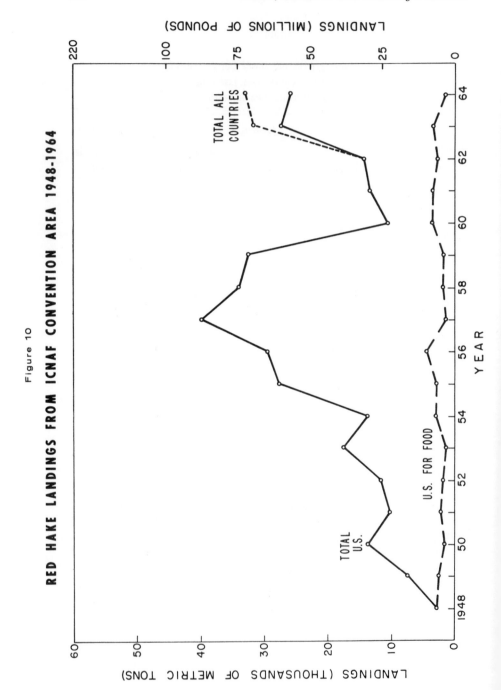

Figure 10

RED HAKE LANDINGS FROM ICNAF CONVENTION AREA 1948-1964

TABLE 11

RED HAKE STATISTICS, ICNAF CONVENTION AREA
(Thousands of Metric Tons, Live Weight) [1]

| Locality of fishing | Landings | | | | Estimated sustainable yield |
	High year	Low year	Average 1952-1964	1964	
Subarea 5					
All countries	38.7 (1957)	8.6 (1960)	30.0	28.2	100
U.S.	38.7 (1957)	8.6 (1960)	29.4	24.6	—

[1] Includes industrial landings.

Industrial Fishery

Landings of fish from the Convention Area by the United States for reduction to meal and oil and for animal food have varied with market demand, reaching high levels in 1956-59 and dropping to lower levels thereafter (Figure 11). The fishery has started to respond to recently improved markets by increasing landings for industrial purposes. Red hake, silver hake, and menhaden make up the bulk of the catch, but a number of other groundfish species are also included.

Table 12 gives values for industrial groundfish other than silver hake and red hake. As much as 31,500 metric tons of these species were taken (in 1957) when the industrial groundfish fishery was very active. We have no estimates of sustainable yield for these species.

TABLE 12

STATISTICS FOR INDUSTRIAL GROUNDFISH, OTHER THAN SILVER HAKE AND RED HAKE, ICNAF CONVENTION AREA
(Thousands of Metric Tons, Live Weight)

| Locality of fishing | Landings | | | | Estimated sustainable yield [1] |
	High year	Low year	Average 1952-1964	1964	
Subarea 5					
All countries	31.5 (1957)	6.1 (1960)	15.8	7.4	—
U.S.	31.5 (1957)	5.7 (1964)	13.1	5.7	—

[1] Probably not fully exploited.

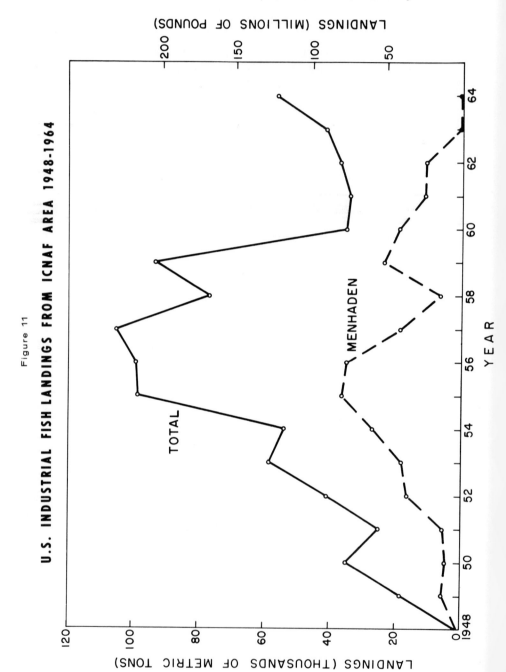

Figure 11

U.S. INDUSTRIAL FISH LANDINGS FROM ICNAF AREA 1948-1964

Other Species

A number of other species are taken in the Convention Area. Statistics concerning them are given in Table 13, but sustainable yields cannot be estimated for these species at this time. Some species may show considerable increases in future years but there is no reason to believe that any of them occur in great quantities.

TABLE 13
STATISTICS FOR OTHER SPECIES, ICNAF CONVENTION AREA
(Thousands of Metric Tons, Live Weight)

Locality of fishing	Landings				Estimated sustainable yield
	High year	Low year	Average 1952-1964	1964	
Pollock					
Subarea 3					
All countries	7.0 (1954)	1.6 (1964)	4.4	1.6	?
U.S.	0	0	0	0	—
Subarea 4					
All countries	33.0 (1962)	2.3 (1954)	23.7	32.3	?
U.S.	3.1 (1959)	1.0 (1957)	1.9	1.2	—
Subarea 5					
All countries	13.6 (1958)	6.1 (1963)	8.9	9.0	?
U.S.	12.3 (1958)	4.7 (1963)	8.1	4.8	—
Other groundfish [1]					
Subarea 5					
All countries	15.8 (1963)	12.4 (1961)	13.7	12.4	?
U.S.	11.7 (1964)	5.9 (1961)	7.1	11.7	—
Swordfish					
Subarea 3					
All countries	1.0 (1963)	0	0.3	0.5	?
U.S.	0	0	—	0	—
Subarea 4					
All countries	4.8 (1963)	1.3 (1961)	2.4	3.5	?
U.S.	NIL				
Subarea 5					
All countries	3.8 (1963)	0.3 (1954)	1.3	3.5	?
U.S.	0.9 (1963)	0.0 (1964)	0.4	0	—

[1] Associated with catches of major groundfish species: dogfish, skate, scup, tautog, sea robin, titefish, wolffish, eelpout, white hake, cusk, ling.

TABLE 13   (Continued)

STATISTICS FOR OTHER SPECIES, ICNAF CONVENTION AREA
(Thousands of Metric Tons, Live Weight)

| Locality of fishing | Landings | | | | Estimated sustainable yield |
	High year	Low year	Average 1952-1964	1964	
Tuna					
Subarea 5					
All countries	3.2 (1962)	0.2 (1956)	1.2	1.2	?
U.S.	3.2 (1962)	0.2 (1956)	1.1	0.8	?
Other pelagic fish—mackerel, butterfish, etc.					
Subarea 3					
All countries	1.3 (1955)	0.0 (1960)	0.5	0.8	?
U.S.	0	0	0	0	—
Subarea 4					
All countries	11.8 (1954)	4.2 (1959)	7.8	10.3	?
U.S.	0	0	0	0	—
Subarea 5					
All countries	7.8 (1963)	2.0 (1961)	3.8	3.1	?
U.S.	4.6 (1958)	1.6 (1961)	3.1	2.2	—
Other miscellaneous fin fish					
Subarea 3					
All countries	14.4 (1955)	5.1 (1961)	9.3	13.7	?
U.S.	0	0	0	0	—
Subarea 4					
All countries	17.2 (1964)	5.9 (1961)	10.6	17.2	?
U.S.	0	0	0	0	—
Subarea 5					
All countries	27.1 (1964)	2.4 (1958)	8.7	27.1	?
U.S.	11.9 (1957)	2.4 (1958)	6.8	6.8	—

Conclusion

Although all the world oceans are theoretically available to New England fishermen, the resource base considered here is taken to be the continental shelf between Rhode Island and Greenland, the area which comes under the jurisdiction of the International Commission for the Northwest Atlantic Fisheries. More specifically, it is that part of the Convention Area which has traditionally been fished by New England vessels (excluding New England whalers), namely, the shelf between Rhode Island and the Grand Bank of Newfoundland.

Increased fishing effort by European countries has increased production from the Convention Area but the U.S. catches have held steady or declined. Some stocks of fish in the Convention Area are fished to capacity and increased exploitation of other stocks is not expected to increase total production more than 20 percent; most of these species are not now highly prized.

New England can increase its landings from the Convention Area by the simple expedient of increasing its fishing effort. This is the method of her foreign competitors. The fish are there but they are taken by Canada and countries distant from the fishing banks. The stocks of valuable species of fish have shown an encouraging stability over the years in spite of the very intensive fishing. Whether or not we have reached the peak of production of these species, the only way we can increase our share is to fish more. The economic problems which have prevented the expansion of the New England fleet must be solved so that the U.S. can send modern efficient vessels to the banks capable of outfishing foreign competitors.

COMMENT

JOHN M. WILKINSON

Federal Reserve Bank of Boston

Until about two days ago, if I had been asked what industry in New England is currently plagued with the most problems, I would have answered, without hesitation, the electric power industry. Power supply and demand, power costs and rates, and blackout problems notwithstanding, after listening to the past two days of discussion here, I am rapidly changing my mind.

The subject of this session—the fisheries resource base and what to do with it—is an extremely difficult one, and one which does not lend itself to precise calculation. However, I cannot fail to observe a few basic similarities (as well as some unique complications) as brought out in Dr. Graham's brief paper and today's presentation, between the fisheries resource and other natural resources generally.

Three points came through rather loud and clear from Dr. Graham's paper and statistical data. One is that we are *not*—as so many publicists would have us believe—dealing with an inexhaustible resource in the Northwest Atlantic fisheries area, or perhaps anywhere, in the intermediate term or the long run. Much is said about the vast wealth of the sea, awaiting exploitation. Dr. Graham points out that, overall, the Northwest Atlantic fishery is probably within 20 percent of having its total sustainable tonnage for all stocks withdrawn, and that some of the more highly-prized species are actually being gradually mined out. This term may seem too alarming in its connotations, but with ever-increasing intensity of fishing—and there is certainly no indication that this intensity will diminish—the fear of over-exploitation seems warranted.

I fully realize that many—if not most of us here—are concerned with the commercial and financial, the sales, the employment, the marketing, and the profit factors of the industry in a localized or regional, as distinct from an international, context. These are valid and necessary concerns which I share. At the same time, Dr. Graham's presentation deals primarily with physical factors—somewhat to my regret for a subject addressed to the resource base. However, he assures me that he is not an economist, but a biologist concerned with fish population. And in this his concern is equally valid.

Nevertheless, between the two problem areas—one business-oriented and one scientifically-oriented—there is an opportunity, even a necessity, for useful contributions to be made from economics, especially when we recognize that we are dealing with a limited, finite supply under an unmanaged—or perhaps incompletely managed—situation. It is certain that maximum physical output is quite a different thing from optimal economic output. There is a long-run price tag associated with each increment of production in terms of an inevitably declining sustainable yield per unit of effort—quite apart from the short-run price tag of factor inputs for labor, boats, and other capital and management items. Therefore, our concern for shifting the demand curve upward and to the right, and our concern for price elasticities, should be matched by a concern for shifting the supply curve outward and to the right as well.

This is not to suggest a preponderance of attention on conservation over mere exploitation. The fishing industry, like the mining and mineral products industry, the forest and wood products industry, and agriculture, is and will continue to be responsive to technological change. It may be possible to increase the fisheries resource enormously—and selectively—*but at a price*. It may also be feasible to broaden the area of harvest—perhaps to include the entire world fishery—but this also can be achieved only *at a price*. What I am suggesting is that *management* of the resource base—as an element of conservation working toward the enhancement of both commercial and scientific interests—will likely require increasing future emphasis.

And this brings out a second point that came through loud and clear from Dr. Graham's statistics. That is the difficulty inherent in management of a common property resource, with unlimited entry, as is the salt water fisheries. I would like to have heard more about the ICNAF convention and its institutional and physical provisos and operations. Perhaps this group is already adequately familiar with them. But it seems virtually impossible to construct meaningful production functions or impose other economic criteria in the face of so elusive a resource base and institutional fact of life. The future evolution of cooperative arrangements in a wider sphere will inevitably demand more attention from the economic community in its role as a bridge between commercial and scientific problems and their solutions, just as will management aspects within our own regional sphere.

The third point for which we have Dr. Graham to thank—and with which I am sure he would be among the first to agree—is the paucity of *really reliable basic* data that reveal sustainable yield, whether for a physical maximum or an economic optimum. The margin of error is admittedly very great at present. We can sample soil for its productivity, count trees for their cordage, and estimate the yield of mines with tolerable accuracy. The extraordinary complexity of the ocean fishery resource, it seems to me, presents a more demanding and challenging task ahead. But, we have mounted, over time, a formidable effort in atmospheric and streamflow hydrology, in geology, and in agronomy and soils sciences. As time goes on, it would seem we should mount a similar effort to determine more precisely the resource here under discussion.

We were indirectly forewarned by the discussion yesterday that this is not the place for elaborating the more elegant and refined economic and statistical tools of the trade for application to the fishing industry, and I think this is right. Nevertheless, they cannot long be ignored, and I would point out at this time that we are dealing here with most of the classic problems of *economics, plus a few more.* Superimposed on the economic problems are the complexities of a common property situation and an indeterminant hydrologic (or oceanographic) variable. The economic variables alone include, among others:

> —multiple and joint products
> —product differentiation—fresh, frozen, etc.
> —product substitution
> —apparently limited supply
> —elasticities and cross-elasticities
> —market area uncertainties
> —industry structure variabilities, or degrees of integration
> —regional and international supplier competition
> —diminishing returns
> —comparative advantages, and
> —seasonality of both demand and supply

It seems apparent therefore that we must become economists as well as scientists and business entrepreneurs. The *land* farmer has had to do precisely this.

All of this is not very immediately helpful, I'm sure. But I might suggest that our problems are somewhat analogous to those faced by water resources—or river basin planners and developers. They have been grappling with multiple and competing demands, limited supply, hydrologic uncertainty and similar technical and economic problems—and with creditable results—for some time. They have formulated and tested (and are perfecting) techniques and methodology for economic maximization under conditions of uncertainty, *with* scientific foundations and *for* commercial clients. Conceivably, under research sponsorship of an agency such as the Bureau of Commercial Fisheries, the in-shore resource analysts' cost-input, input-output, and output-benefit functional relationships may in time be appropriate for translation from river-basin analysis to—shall we say—sea-basin analysis. With such an effort—or perhaps with sea-grant colleges as proposed along the lines of land-grant colleges, we may come to know more about the fisheries resource base and what to do with it. As one of you mentioned yesterday, we are still *hunters*, not *farmers*, and we are 100 years behind agriculture—in a technologic sense. Even so, I'm inclined to side with Mr. Crowther, by viewing the outlook with a degree of cautious optimism.

THE INTERACTION BETWEEN
TWO FISH POPULATIONS
AND THEIR MARKETS

A PRELIMINARY REPORT *

HARLAN C. LAMPE**

University of Rhode Island

The evaluation of equilibrium conditions in exploited fisheries has been an important area of activity for both fishery biologists and economists. A considerable literature exists concerning the biological characteristics of equilibrium and a more limited literature exists concerning economic equilibrium. Early efforts to develop an economic theory of fishery exploitation by Turvey, Scott, and Gordon have been extended, formalized, and evaluated by Crutchfield and Zellner.[1] This work treats a series of interesting problems and specifically concerns itself with a single market for a single species under static market conditions.

In evaluating changes in technology, Crutchfield and Zellner bring oscillatory or non-equilibrating conditions to the fore and state:

> It is indeed interesting to observe that in a model without logarithms and with no oscillatory impressed force the approximate solution is characterized by an oscillatory component the characteristics of which, unfortunately, can not be specified precisely, given present inadequate knowledge of the values of parameters in the model.[2]

*Contribution No. 1176 of College of Agriculture, University of Rhode Island.
**Associate Professor of Food and Resource Economics.
[1] James Crutchfield and Arnold Zellner, "Economic Aspects of the Pacific Halibut Fishery," *Fishery Industrial Research,* Vol. 1, No. 1, (April 1962). See Appendix 1, pp. 112-117.
[2] *Ibid.,* p. 115.

This statement, in essence, is a point of departure for this paper, the purpose of which is to discuss the stability of, and stability conditions for, two independent fisheries conjoined by two mutually dependent markets. It is necessary to emphasize that this is in the nature of a progress report of a study in an early stage of development. Since both an economic and biological model are welded into a single model here, choices had to be made concerning the kinds of models to be employed in each case.

The Biological Model. This is hardly the field in which an economist can or will pretend to any particular expertise. However, it is important that the model chosen contain certain characteristics. Among these are:

1) A sufficient number of parameters to permit an interesting range of changes in the nature of the populations. Among the parameters of interest to economists and biologists alike are:
   a) natural mortality rates
   b) growth rates
   c) recruitment
   d) fishing mortality rates

These, among others, can help distinguish one population from another.

2) A form susceptible of modification for density dependent relations.

3) A form susceptible of modification to include random variation in the variables and parameters.

The population model selected certainly possesses the first characteristic and appears to possess the latter two. It is presented below.[3]

$$_x Y_w = F_x R' W\infty \sum_{n=0}^{3} \Omega_n \frac{e^{-nK(t_p' - t_0)}\left(1 - e^{-(F_x + M + nK)}\right)}{F_x + M + nK} \left\{ \left(\frac{1 - e^{-(F_0 + M + nK)(\lambda - X)}}{1 - e^{-(F_0 + M + nK)}} \right) \times \right.$$

$$\left. e^{-(M + nK)X} - \sum_{u=0}^{X-1} F_u + \sum_{q=0}^{X-1} e^{-(M + nK)q} - \sum_{u=X-q}^{X-1} F_u \right\}$$

[3] R. J. H. Beverton, and S. J. Holt, *On The Dynamics of Exploited Fish Populations* (London: H.M.S.O., 1957), p. 85.

where,

$_x Y_w$ = Weight yield in year X, in grams
F_x = Fishing mortality rate in year X, also (F_u)
R' = Recruitment in numbers
W_∞ = Maximum weight of fish in grams
Ω_n = Constants, n = 0,1,2,3
e = Base of Naperian logarithms
K = Growth of coefficient
M = Natural mortality rate
F_o = Initial, steady state, fishing mortality rate
λ = Maximum age of fish
$t_{p'}$ = Age of fish at recruitment
t_o = Age at origin
X = Integer indicating year (or any time period)

The equation above is used to determine yield for the first $\lambda - 1$ years after initial state. The equation below is used to compute yield for years λ onward.

$$_x Y_w = F_x R' W_\infty \sum_{n=0}^{3} \frac{\Omega_n e^{-nK(t_{p'} - t_o)} \left(1 - e^{-(F_X + M + nK)}\right)}{F_x + M + nK} X$$

$$\sum_{q=0}^{\lambda - 1} e^{-(M + nK)q} - \sum_{u = X - q}^{X - 1} F_u$$

The basic relation between the population model and an economic model is through the rate of fishing mortality. The same basic model will be used for both populations. The populations will be distinguishable by means of their parameters. Thus the economic model to be related must include some relation that influences the rate of fishing mortality.

The Economic Model. The economic model is a simple one based upon a rather conventional cobweb approach to a dynamic market. Two markets must be constructed and these markets will be interrelated.

The demand function in the first market is:

$$\ln P_{1t} = a_1 + a_{11} \ln {}_t Y_{1w} + a_{12} \ln P_{2t}$$

where: P_{1t} = Price of fish 1 in time t

$\quad\quad {}_t Y_{1w}$ = Weight yield of fish 1 in pounds x 10^{-3}

$\quad\quad P_{2t}$ = Price of fish 2 in time t

The demand function in the second market is:

$$\ln P_{2t} = a_2 + a_{21} \ln {}_t Y_{2w} + a_{22} \ln P_{1t}$$

$\quad {}_t Y_{2w}$ = Weight yield of fish 2 in pounds x 10^{-3}

The supply side of both markets requires some explanation and perhaps considerable improvement. The primary determinant of yield ($_t Y_w$) in any time, t, is the current rate of fishing mortality and the past history of mortality rates. The supply side of the market must influence this mortality rate.

Assume that it is the case that the current rate of fishing mortality is a function of effort expended in fishing. Specifically, that:

$$_1 F_{1X} = {}_1 F_t = C_1 \, _1 E_t$$

which is to say fishing mortality is a linear function of effort with some coefficient, C.

Further assume that effort is related to income. Specifically, effort is a function of income in the previous time period as follows:

$$E_{1t} = a_{1t-1} Y_{w1} \, P_{1t-1} = a_1 \, R_{1t-1}$$

again a linear relation.

However, if total effort in any time period, t, is restrained, as it is where the number of vessels cannot be changed, we then have:

$$E_t = E_{1t} + E_{2t}$$

A problem then is one of dividing the total effort among E_{1t}, E_{2t}, and E_O, where E_O is unexpended effort. If $E_O = 0$, the relation above holds. We can examine the influence of both conditions, i.e., $E_O = 0$ and $E_O > 0$.

With some substitution we get a relation:

$$_1F_t = C_1 (a_1 F_{1t-1}) = C_1 a_1 R_{1t-1}$$

which leaves $_1F_t$ relatively unrestrained. Another formulation might be:

$$_1F_t = C_1 a_1 R_{1t-1} / R_{t-1}$$

$$(\text{where: } R_t = R_{1t} + R_{2t})$$

Thus we have fishing mortality proportional to the share of revenue produced by the fish. This is tantamount to saying that effort will be distributed in such a way that average value productivities are equal. This could be construed to imply (if the functions are assumed linear) that effort is distributed in such a way that marginal value productivities are equal in both fisheries.

The relationships of effort, fishing mortality, and revenue will need considerable analysis and evaluation before a fixed commitment can be made. However, for the purposes of this paper, the relationships:

$$_1F_t = C_1 a_1 R_{1t-1} / R_{t-1} = b_1 R_{1t-1} / R_{t-1}$$

$$_2F_t = C_2 a_2 R_{2t-1} / R_{t-1} = b_2 R_{2t-1} / R_{t-1}$$

will be used. To reflect the case where $E_O = 0$, and $_1F_t + _2F_t = K$ (a constant), $b_1 = b_2$.

To recapitulate:

The demand equations are:

Fish 1: $\ln P_{1t} = a_1 + a_{11} \ln {}_tY_{1w} + a_{12} \ln P_{2t}$

Fish 2: $\ln P_{2t} = a_2 + a_{21} \ln {}_tY_{2w} + a_{22} \ln P_{1t}$

The supply equations are those presented above where:

$$_1^F X = b_1 \, R_{1t-1} / R_{t-1}$$

$$_2^F X = b_2 \, R_{2t-1} / R_{t-1}$$

Parameter Values. The choice of parameter values for the model is arbitrary. However, values have been chosen that are not unreasonable in magnitude. Since the matter of principal concern is the effect upon paths by which the model achieves stability and the relationship of these paths to various parameter values, the precise values of the coefficients are of somewhat less importance than they would be were we interested in the values of the variables (price, yield, and returns) *per se*.

It is best to consider both fish and markets hypothetical although the population characteristics are based upon data in Beverton and Holt,[4] and the market parameters are based upon work by the author and J. F. Farrell.[5] Table 1 illustrates a set of parameter values.

TABLE 1

**PARAMETER AND VARIABLE VALUES FOR
TWO FISH POPULATIONS AND MARKETS ***

Parameter or Variable	Fish 1	Fish 2
R' (recruitment, nos.)	$.35 \times 10^8$	$.70 \times 10^8$
W_∞ (max. wt., gms.)	2867.	2867.
K (growth coeff.)	.095	.095
M (nat. mort. rate)	.25	.25
F_0 (steady state fish mort.)	.115	.172
λ (max. age, yrs.)	15.	15.
t_e' (age at recruit.)	3.72	3.72
t_0 (origin age, yrs.)	−.815	−.815
a_i (demand cost.)	5.6058	4.9798
a_{i1} (demand slope)	−.4505	−.3168
a_{i2} (other price coeff.)	.3900	.3971
b_i (fish mort. coeff.)	.46	.23

* Parameter values from Beverton & Holt *op. cit.* and Farrell & Lampe *op. cit.*

[4] *Op. cit.*

[5] J. F. Farrell and H. C. Lampe "The New England Fishing Industry: Functional Markets for Finned Food Fish II" *R. I. Agricultural Experiment Station Bulletin* No. 380, June, 1965.

The attached figures illustrate the behavior of the markets and revenue. The bottom section of Figure 1 shows changes in fishing mortality (fish 1 denoted by 1, and fish 2 by 2) along with total revenue.

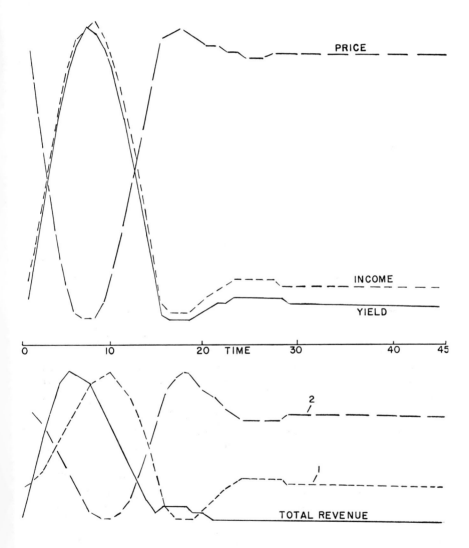

FIGURE 1. Top: Price, income, and yield for fish 1 given parameters of Table 1.
Bottom: Instantaneous fishing mortality rates for fish 1 and fish 2 with total revenue from both fish.

The top section of Figure 1 shows the behavior of prices (p), income (I), and yield (Y), for the first fish; Figure 1A gives the same information for fish 2.

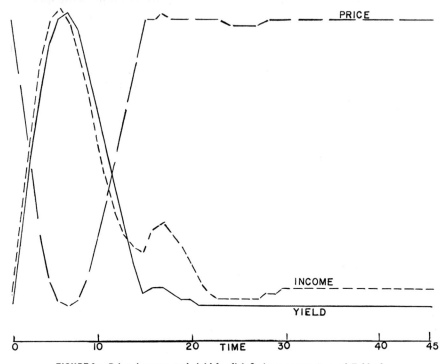

FIGURE 1a. Price, income, and yield for fish 2 given parameters of Table 1.

The lines do not all measure the same things and scales are not presented. Since these lines primarily illustrate the time path of change (and proportionate change, at that), they are primarily useful in assessing leads and lags and in determining the length of time before, and if, stability is achieved. Forty-five time periods are shown in Figure 1, and almost 30 were required before stability was achieved.

A matter of considerable interest, the rationale for which is not yet clear, is that despite the fact that the steady state fishing mortalities selected were (by design) precisely the equilibrium values, the pressure of the market and interactions with the population were such that considerable variation occurred before the situation stabilized.

Figures 2 and 2A illustrate a condition where the price of fish 1 is increasingly dependent upon fish 2, i.e., a_{12} was changed from

.39 to .50. Notice particularly in Figure 2A that the behavior during the first 17 time periods differs significantly from that shown in 1A. A relatively steady condition is achieved in about 30 time periods.

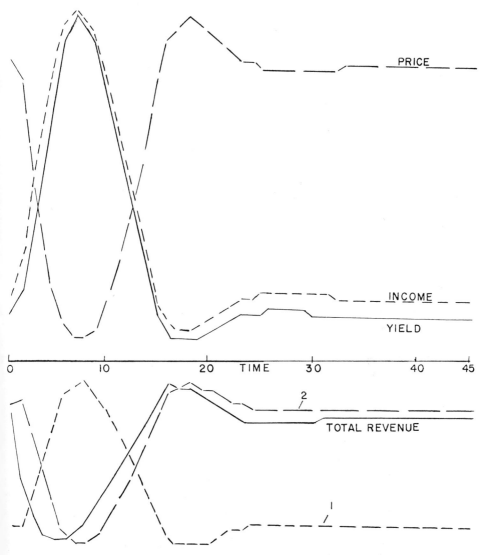

FIGURE 2. Top: Price, income, and yield for fish 1 given $a_{12} = .50$, other parameters as in Table 1.

Bottom: Instantaneous fishing mortality rates for fish 1 and fish 2 with total revenue from both fish.

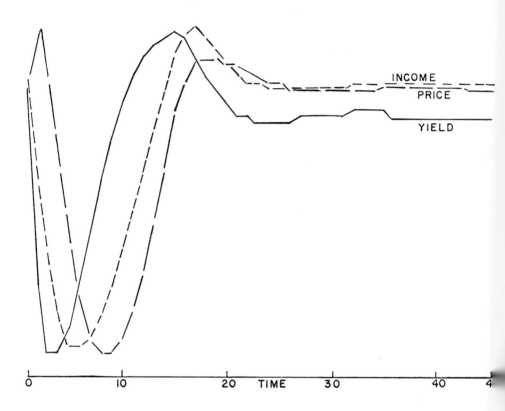

FIGURE 2a. Price, income and yield for fish 2 given $a_{12} = .50$, other parameters as in Table 1.

    In contrast, Figures 3 and 3A show a quickly stabilizing circum-
stance where all parameters are as in Table 1, save a_{11} which is
$-.60$ (as compared to $-.4505$). Under conditions shown in Figures
3 and 3A, stability is generated in 13 time periods. The change in
a_{11} represents a significant decline in elasticity. Where demand
elasticities for the two fish are disparate, stability is much more
quickly achieved. It should be noted that the characteristics of the
two populations are identical but for size.

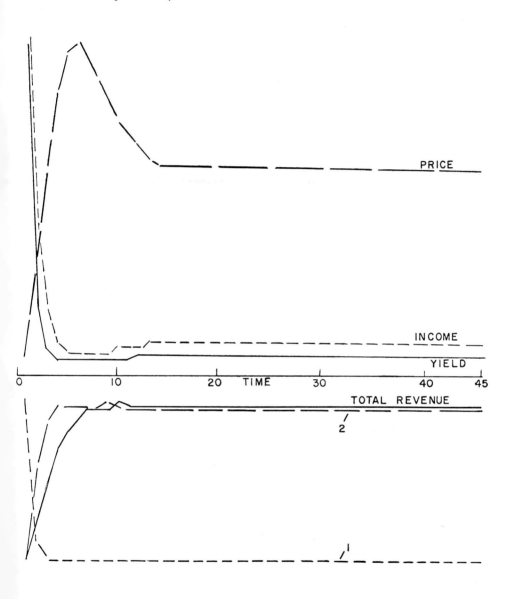

FIGURE 3. **Top:** Price, income and yield for fish 1 given $a_{11} = -.60$, other parameters as in Table 1.

Bottom: Instantaneous fishing mortality rates for fish 1 and fish 2 with total revenue from both fish.

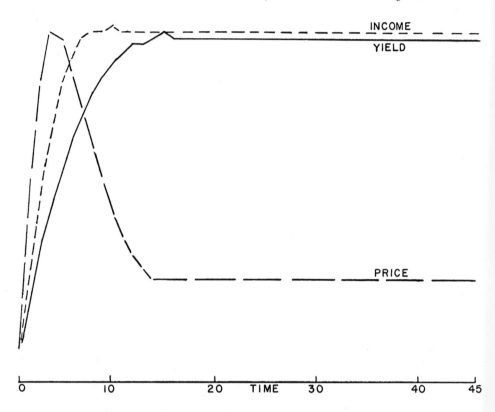

FIGURE 3a. Price, income, and yield for fish 2 given $a_{11} = -.60$, other parameters as in Table 1.

The performance of the model under the three sets of conditions suggests several problems of a practical nature. An important one is that the length of time required to achieve stability after changes in the system can complicate, if not invalidate, many measures of population characteristics. Another is that the speed of adjustment is not a function of the population characteristics alone, but related in an important way to market characteristics.

Figures 4 and 4A illustrate a condition where only M_1 (natural mortality) differs from the original parameters in Table 1. In this case $M_1 = .10$ (was .25). Notice that 35 time periods are required to achieve stability. Thus, not only will changes in mortality rates (and other population parameters) influence the level of equilibrium, but also the time required to achieve it.

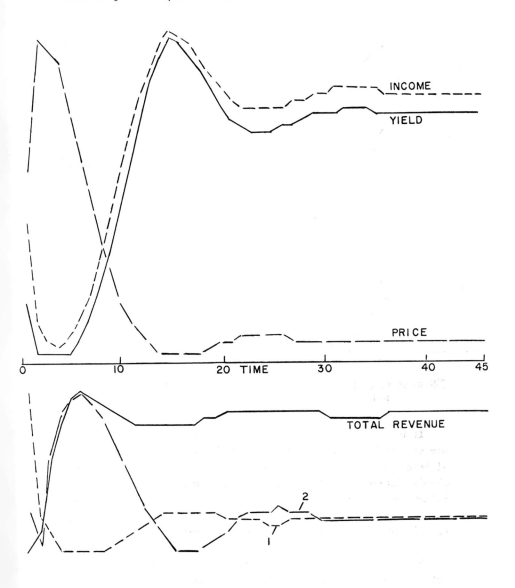

FIGURE 4. Top: Price, income, and yield for fish 1 given $M_1 = .10$, other parameters as in Table 1.

Bottom: Instantaneous fishing mortality rates for fish 1 and fish 2 with total revenue from both fish.

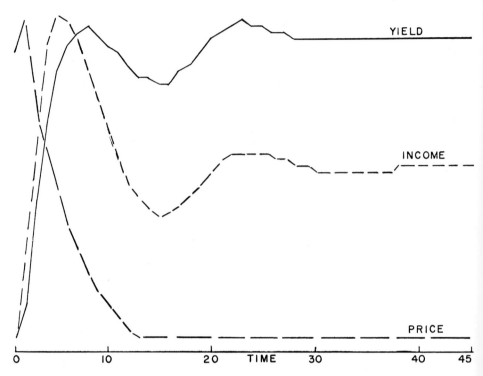

FIGURE 4a. Price, income, and yield for fish given $M_1 = .10$, other parameters as in Table 2.

It is important to state here that where fisheries and markets are essentially independent the adjustment period rarely exceeded 11 time periods. The location of equilibrium was, however, dramatically changed in many cases depending upon population and market characteristics.

Conclusions and Suggestions for Further Work

Several conclusions are suggested by this analysis of the interactions between two fish populations and their markets.

First, conclusions drawn concerning equilibrium conditions and paths followed to achieve stability from previous models of isolated fisheries may well be erroneous. The time required to stabilize in the two fishery model is normally longer than that required to achieve stability for an isolated fishery having identical characteristics.

Second, changes in fishing intensity brought about by changing market conditions may have long lasting effects upon the population. This fact points out the difficulties faced by biologists in assaying population parameters of an exploited fishery.

Third, where a population model is coupled with an economic model, as it is here, the influence of some parameters is more important than others. Those parameters which influence the approach to stability and the stability conditions would appear to be the ones to which most attention should be devoted. Those parameters that influence solutions very little can perhaps be ignored, or at least their estimation postponed, until more critical parameters are evaluated.

Continuing work needs to be done in recognizing the potential density dependent nature of many variables. This will be the next phase of this study. Perhaps the most important change required in the model is explicit recognition of its stochastic nature. To affect a more precise reflection of the real conditions, specific cognizance will be given such obvious fluctuations as occur in recruitment. In addition, every effort should be made to permit random fluctuation in both biological and economic parameters.

COMMENT

HARVEY M. HUTCHINGS

Bureau of Commercial Fisheries

Time has not permitted adequate reflections on a paper with so many dimensions as this. I do, however, have a few comments which might be appropriate.

Professor Lampe deserves credit for his attempt to integrate the realities of physical fish populations, the factors associated with their exploitations, and the restrictions of markets in space, into a single model. By using a model supposedly approximating the real situation faced by decision makers in the industry, the computer can utilize a wealth of data in generating predictions of yields, prices and revenues through time. This model is more dynamic than most others with which I am familiar. It is dynamic in the sense that it generates results for each time period which depend upon results and conditions for all earlier time periods.

Much background work is necessary for an analysis of this type. Think of all the data that are needed for the various components or elements of the model.

1. For population predictions from one time period to the next, Professor Lampe took into account recruitment of new individuals into the population, growth of individuals in the population, capture of individuals from the population, and losses due to "natural death" occurring within the population.

2. For supply relationships much data concerning relative catches, efforts, and revenues among the fisheries are needed in various time periods.

3. Finally, for demand functions, estimates are needed for price-quantity relationships and the relationships among the various fish products.

All of these elements are based on great amounts of data and information from a great many sources. Even after these data are obtained, getting them into the proper form and incorporating them into a final workable model is no simple matter.

In spite of the complexities of this model, however, it still is simplified in that it considers only two markets and two fish populations when in fact there are seldom this few to be considered in the real life situation. As has been pointed out, this is a progress report. Professor Lampe's work to date has been largely hypothetical. But, it does set the stage for perfecting the more general model incorporating more of the conditions of real life. I hope he will press forward with this work.

One word of caution is appropriate at this point. This model is quite mathematical and employs some rather advanced techniques. Its success and practical usefulness depends, however, on accurate data. This is very basic to all analyses of this type and it cannot be over-emphasized that the results can be no better than the data which go into them. Professor Lampe's work to date has been theoretical in terms of the development of a workable model. He has indicated that he has few results of practical value at this time. Further, his work to date is concerned with the stability aspects of the industry rather than with the level of yields, prices, revenues, and so forth. For this reason I hesitate to comment on his data. However, I would question whether or not he can bypass in a sense the level of yield, prices, and revenues and move on to the problem of stability. Would not the level of these parameters affect the conditions of stability?

I would mention two other points related to his work. First, he has indicated that it takes several years, in some cases as much as 35, to reach stability. I am afraid that we experience changes frequently enough in demand, supply and in the characteristics of the population, all of which affect the stability of the industry, that we would continually be in a period of instability. The other point is that I am not sure what the conditions of stability are. Are they at the point of maximum sustainable yield? Are they at the point of maximum profit to the industry? This is not clear in the paper.

I would hope that in his further work, Professor Lampe would devote some attention to a consideration of fish populations which are dependent in the sense that if one population does not prey upon the other they at least compete for food. This seems more realistic, particularly where fishing effort in one population interacts with the effort in the other population. Also, I would hope that the demand equation could be improved to include shifters such as the number of consumers, consumer incomes, and so forth.

We need to continue our work on such models and test them with respect to their predictive ability. Only in this manner can the uncertainty of the future be overcome in such a way that capital can be invested and managed on something better than a trial-and-error basis, and under less ulcer-creating circumstances. With increasing capital requirements per economic unit of production in our advancing society of big business, better methods of predicting the future are becoming a necessity. More and more segments of business and industry have computer technology available to them and thus are able to utilize a wealth of data in their sophisticated and calibrated business decisions.

The fishing industry is no exception. If it is to survive and compete within our economy for labor, investment capital, and even for markets, it must look forward to utilizing these tools of management which are being used by other segments of the economy. Time can well be spent on the perfection of these models. All of us don't have to be mathematicians or econometricians to appreciate the usefulness of these models as long as they do the job for which they were designed.

A STUDY OF POLICY CONSIDERATIONS
IN MANAGING THE
GEORGES BANK HADDOCK FISHERY

LAWRENCE W. VAN MEIR

Bureau of Commercial Fisheries

Fishery management is one of the most complex and serious problems facing the commercial fishing industry today. Moreover, this problem likely will become more serious in the future. The world catch of fish and shellfish has doubled approximately every 10 years during the past 30 years. And, this increase in catch has been confined largely to a limited group of species of fish. Thus, the fishing pressure on certain stocks has been increasing rapidly and likely will continue to increase in the future—not only due to expanded effort on the part of several of the major fishing nations but also due to the entry of new nations into the fisheries. Without doubt, conservation measures will have to be applied to additional species of fish in the near future.

Crutchfield and Zellner have defined fishery management as ". . . control exercised by public authority over fishing activities." [1] There seems to be little doubt that a management program for high seas fisheries will have to be administered by the Federal Government. In the first place, in order for industry to conduct an effective management program, it would have to have the authority and power to regulate and police its activities. However, the courts have held a firm line against legislation permitting such self-regulation on the part of industry. Second, management of high seas

---

[1] James Crutchfield and Arnold Zellner, "Economic Aspects of the Pacific Halibut Fishery," *Fishery Industrial Research*, Vol. 1, No. 1, (April, 1962).

fisheries involves negotiations and agreements with foreign nations which clearly are a responsibility of the Federal Government.

The complex and difficult aspect of fishery management hinges around the objectives to be achieved by the control to be exercised. To date, conservation programs have been instituted to achieve mainly a biological goal, namely, to prevent fishing effort from exceeding the level commensurate with maximum sustainable yield or, to rebuild a fishery population to the level which will yield the maximum annual harvest. Pioneering works by such economists as Gordon, Scott, Crutchfield and Zellner, Turvey, and Christy have highlighted the economic aspects of fishery management. The basis for fishery management was cleverly stated by Dr. Martin Burkenroad as "The management of fisheries is intended for the benefit of man, not fish; therefore, effect of management upon fish stocks cannot be regarded as beneficial per se."[2]

This then brings us to the central theme of this paper: what are the policy alternatives to consider in drafting a program of fishery management and what are the economic benefits and consequences that may accompany each individual policy? To bring this closer to home, we will view these policy alternatives in relation to the Georges Bank haddock fishery.

The Georges Bank Haddock Fishery

Georges Bank is an area of relatively shallow water to the east of Nantucket. In approximate terms, it represents an area of about 21,000 square miles lying between 40 degrees and 42 degrees North latitude and 66 degrees and 69 degrees West longitude. The Bank is surrounded by deep water which confines the haddock population to the Bank. Thus, the Georges Bank haddock fishery consists of non-migratory population of haddock which provides a well-defined distinct fishery.

Georges Bank has provided over 75 percent of the total U.S. landings of haddock in recent years. For the 10 years, 1954-1963, the U.S. fishing industry has taken an average of 45.8 million pounds of haddock annually from the Bank, representing an average ex-vessel value of $7.6 million. This places the Georges Bank haddock fishery among the top two most valuable resources for the New England fishing industry.

---

[2] Martin D. Burkenroad, "Theory and Practice of Marine Fishery Management," *Journal du Conseil Permanent International pour L'exploration de la Mer*, Vol. XVIII, No. 3, (January, 1953).

TABLE 1

CATCH AND VALUE OF HADDOCK FOR GEORGES BANK
AND U.S. TOTAL 1953-1963

Year	Haddock Catch on Georges Bank		Value of Catch on Georges Bank [2] $	Total U.S. Landing	% of U.S. Catch from Georges Bank
	Total	U.S. [1]			
1953	44,630	44,630	7,422	63,324	70.5
1954	46,639	46,639	6,647	70,278	66.4
1955	42,255	43,224	5,719	61,252	70.6
1956	51,144	51,144	7,104	69,059	74.1
1957	48,561	48,561	8,169	60,588	80.1
1958	37,321	37,231	8,072	54,230	68.8
1959	36,037	36,037	7,712	51,088	70.5
1960	40,862	40,785	7,105	53,841	75.6
1961	46,483	46,350	7,579	62,414	76.5
1962	53,973	49,378	8,850	60,895	81.1
1963	54,822	44,126	9,088	56,233	78.5

[1] Landing in metric tons
[2] Value in thousands of dollars

We have data on landings and value of haddock going back to 1890. Since 1926, rather complete records are available on the amount of fishing effort and the catch of haddock on Georges Bank. These data have enabled fishing biologists to draw inferences as to the nature of the dynamics of the haddock population of this fishery. Dick Hennemuth, Bureau of Commercial Fisheries biologist at the Woods Hole Biological Laboratory, has made a preliminary estimate of the relationship between the catch per day of fishing effort and the total number of days of fishing effort applied to the Georges Bank haddock fishery (see Chart 1). This preliminary regression equation is:

Equation 1:

$$\frac{L/D}{1,000} = 37.3 - 3.53 \frac{D}{1,000}$$

Where:

L = landings of haddock from Georges Bank
D = days of fishing effort for haddock on Georges Bank

CHART 1

GEORGES BANK HADDOCK

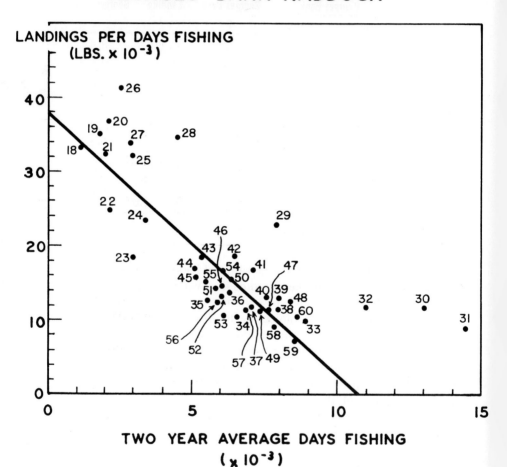

LANDINGS PER DAYS FISHING
(LBS. x 10⁻³)

TWO YEAR AVERAGE DAYS FISHING
(x 10⁻³)

Although this is a preliminary estimate, and the data must be further analyzed, this will serve to illustrate the aspects of policy for fishery management that we want to consider. Thus, according to this relationship, an increase in total fishing effort of 1,000 days will tend to decrease the catch per day of fishing effort by 3,530 pounds. Disregarding the conservation aspect for a moment, it is obvious that as fishing effort continues to increase, the cost per ton of haddock caught will tend to increase due to the drop in the yield per day of fishing effort. Thus, it is possible that, in spite of the best efforts of the individual fishing firm to be efficient in its fishing operations, it may be operating in the red as a result of a general increase in fishing effort. This situation is an industry-wide problem over which the individual firm has no control or relief.

If we take equation 1 and multiply through successively by 1,000 and by D, we obtain an expression for the total landings of haddock as a function of the total amount of fishing effort (See Chart 2). This equation becomes:

Equation 2:

$$L = 37,300 \, D - 3.53 \, D^2$$

Where:

L = total landings of haddock in pounds

D = total fishing effort in days.

This equation is a second degree parabola, passing through the point of origin and open in the direction of the negative axis of landings.

We can now arrive at an estimate of the total number of days of fishing effort that likely will produce the maximum sustainable yield and estimate the total annual yield of the fishery at the level of fishing effort. Taking the first derivative of Equation 2 with respect to days of fishing effort we obtain the expression:

Equation 3:

$$L' = 37,300 - 7.06 \, D$$

Setting this derivative equal to 0 and solving for D we obtain an estimate of 5,283 or approximately 5,300 as the number of days of fishing effort which will yield the maximum sutainable yield of haddock on Georges Bank with the present fishing technology. Substituting 5,300 days of fishing effort in equation 2 gives an estimate for the maximum sustainable yield of approximately 98.5 million pounds. Thus, if fishing effort is maintained for a period of years at a level substantially above or below 5,300 days, the annual harvest likely would be less than 98.5 million pounds (44,700 metric tons).

CHART 2

HADDOCK YIELD IN RELATION TO
FISHING EFFORT on GEORGES BANK

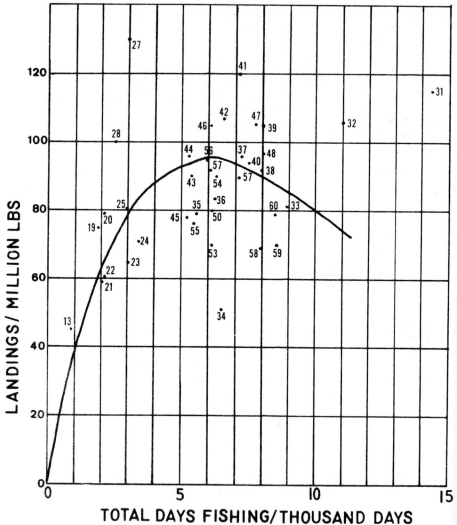

TOTAL DAYS FISHING/THOUSAND DAYS

(2 YEAR AVERAGE)

Now for the purpose of tackling the management problem, let us assume that the above figures represent the true population relationships for the Georges Bank haddock fishery. If the fishery continues to be unregulated, increasing population and income may result in a steadily rising demand for haddock resulting in a continuous upward pressure on price. An increasing price for haddock would tend to yield temporary profits in fishing and would encourage an expansion of fishing effort. If the increase in demand continues long enough, and the price of haddock rises sufficiently, it is obvious that the total fishing effort likely would surpass the level which would yield the maximum sustainable yield of the resource. Thus, eventually the consuming public would actually have less haddock available at a higher price than if the fishing effort were curtailed at the level of maximum sustainable yield.

Preliminary analysis indicates that the demand for haddock, at least throughout the range of relative quantities, is somewhat elastic. That is to say, for each 10 percent increase in the volume of haddock placed on the market, price need only be reduced by something less than 10 percent to move the increased volume into consumption. Thus the total revenue (total value of sales) will tend to increase as the volume sold increases. Hence, total revenue will reach a maximum when the fishery is being operated at the level of maximum sustainable yield.

With no restriction on fishing effort, the industry may tend to arrive at an equilibrium at some level of fishing effort beyond the maximum yield with revenue just covering cost, but at a level of revenue lower than could be attained by reducing effort and increasing the total quantity of fish taken. This is illustrated by the point OE_1 on Chart 3. It might even be possible that fishing effort would be pushed out to point OE_2 on Chart 3, where the total cost would exceed the total revenue and still have the fishery being overfished for a considerable period of time. The loss in this case is not an out-of-pocket loss but represents either low earnings on the part of fishermen, low earnings to invested capital, inability to offset depreciation of capital equipment, or a combination of all three. Thus, we find that for the period 1959-63, hourly earnings for many fishermen in the Boston offshore trawling fleet averaged less than $2.00 per hour

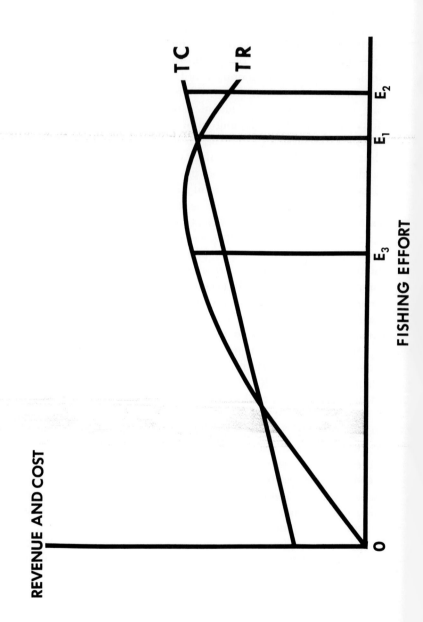

CHART 3

REVENUE AND COST OF FISHING EFFORT

REVENUE AND COST

TC

TR

O

E₃

E₁

E₂

FISHING EFFORT

and many vessels were unable to realize sufficient earnings above variable costs to offset a depreciation charge against the replacement cost of the vessel. In the latter case, where the industry is operating at a loss, it is evident that the firms in the industry would be better off if fishing effort were curtailed to the level of maximum sustainable yield.

In summary then, there is a basis for a valid public interest in controlling fishing effort in those cases where conditions in the industry would lead to over-fishing. If then, we institute a program of management, what goals shall we establish for this management program?

Policy Alternatives for Management

As background for analyzing the relative merits and shortcomings of alternative policies, what criteria should we establish for performance on the part of the commercial fishing industry? I will not take time to elaborate on all criteria for industry within the framework of a "Free Enterprise System," but three criteria are of extreme importance for our consideration today.

1. *Efficiency of Production*—The industry should utilize labor and capital in that combination that will minimize the cost of production for each level of output.

2. *Efficiency in Distribution*—The industry should market the product in the manner that will maximize the total revenue at each level of output.

3. *Economic Development*—The industry should contain incentives that will encourage the development and adoption of new and more efficient technology over time.

In light of these criteria, let's consider three policy alternatives for fishery management. These three policy alternatives are: Freedom of Entry, Maximum Net Profit Over Costs, and Maximum Employment of Labor and Capital.

Establishing freedom of entry as a policy goal means that we adopt as public policy the principle that fishery resources are common property resources and as such should be open to all who care to exploit them. Therefore, in order to conserve the resource in fisheries where normal conditions would lead to over-fishing, it would be necessary to establish an annual quota of fish equivalent to the estimated maximum sustainable yield and then simply to close the fishery as the annual quota was reached. This program of management is quite direct and productive in terms of conserving the resource but does nothing to correct the economic problems of the fishery. In fact, the economic problems may tend to be aggravated. There may be a general tendency for firms to enter the fishery to get their share of the quota before the fishery is closed. The net result may be an extremely short fishing season with a resulting lower average ex-vessel price for fish. Therefore, the total revenue to the industry may decline and costs rise, thus further aggravating the low earning position of the industry, or turning an otherwise reasonably tenable cost-revenue situation into a clear loss proposition.

For example, assume the 100 million pounds of annual harvest of haddock from Georges Bank were landed in a period of 4 months. The ex-vessel price for haddock during this period might average no more than 7 cents a pound with gross revenue of only $7 million. Furthermore, the total cost likely would be greater because of the large influx of vessels and fishermen to land the 100 million pounds in 4 months, let alone the increased cost for processing and distribution. On the other hand, this 100 million pounds of fish, if marketed in an orderly manner throughout the year, might earn an average ex-vessel price of 12 cents a pound representing a total revenue of $12 million. Thus, if we adopted a policy of freedom of entry in managing the Georges Bank haddock fishery, we could expect to conserve the resource but could well maintain the industry in a low earning and constantly depressed condition.

The goal of freedom of entry might be considered as one extreme of the spectrum of policy alternatives. As the other extreme, we might establish the goal of obtaining the maximum net revenue above the costs for labor and capital. This situation can be demonstrated graphically by OE_3 on Chart 3.

The amount of profit (i.e. the net earnings above capital and labor costs) is represented by the vertical distance between the cost line and the revenue curve. Inasmuch as the increase in revenue will be small with each increase in fishing effort as the maximum sustainable yield is approached, the maximum net profit will occur at some level of effort below that necessary to produce the maximum sustainable yield. This outcome can be identified as the monopoly result. In other words, if a monopoly were granted to an individual or fishing firm, the firm could be expected to seek the maximum profit position. We would assume that the monopolist would strive to be as efficient as possible in both minimizing the costs of harvesting, processing, and distributing as well as seeking the marketing pattern that would maximize revenue from the resource.

Clearly the Federal Government is not going to grant a monopoly privilege to any firm to exploit a fishing resource. In fact we have laws that seek as their goal the prevention of monopolies developing. The task of administering a regulatory program to achieve the results of monopoly operation of an industry would not only be extremely difficult and hazardous, but would in effect be contrary to other public goals where we expect competition in our economy to determine the level of output, prices, and allocation of labor and capital among the economic alternatives. In other words, there seems to be no justification from the viewpoint of public policy for holding the employment of labor and capital in a fishery to a level below what that fishery could absorb at the opportunity costs for these inputs.

It seems to me that the relevant area of policy falls somewhere between these two extremes. Perhaps we might term this the goal of achieving the maximum employment of labor and capital at going rates of return for these resources. Thus there would be no need to halt fishing effort short of the maximum sustainable yield as long as any increase in fishing effort would return a sufficient remuneration to the labor and capital involved. However, we would still be interested in assuring that we are operating on the highest possible revenue curve, that is, that the fish are being moved into the highest value use and that the distribution of landings throughout the year will result in the highest possible average ex-vessel price for fish.

It would also be in the interest of the public to insure that the firms included in the fishery were efficient in their fishing operations. One possible means of accomplishing this might be to establish a quota of fishing effort rather than fish. The units of fishing effort would be licensed out to fishing firms until the total quota was exhausted. The fishing rights would also be transferable. Thus the more efficient fishing firms could afford to buy up units of fishing effort from the less efficient fishing firms and consequently a means of encouraging efficiency would result. It is true that this procedure would capitalize the economic profit obtainable in the fishery into value of the fishing right, thus yielding a windfall profit to those initially granted fishing rights. However, in time this would become incorporated as a part of the cost of fishing. On the other hand, any individual firm can improve its own earning position by improved management or improved techniques of fishing. Thus this method would also encourage adoption of new technological developments by the industry.

Furthermore, the individual firm would be under no pressure to concentrate its fishing effort in a short period of time to try and capture a "lion's share" of the fish—for it would know that the fish would be available at whatever time of the year and rate it cared to apply its quota of fishing effort. The individual firm now can turn its attention to more refined problems of management such as, what would be the most profitable allocation of fishing effort— as among the various months of the year as well as between fishing its quota of haddock along with effort expended on other species of fish. This might well result in the development of a flexible fishing fleet in which the spacing of fishing effort over the year was achieved by rotating trips for haddock with trips for other species rather than by tie-ups and idle vessel time.

The problem becomes much more complex when we consider a management program between a number of nations, though the same general argument applies. However, there appears to be no good remedy for the case of the country that decides to underwrite a substantial part of the industry's cost of fishing through subsidies. In this case, only two alternatives appear feasible: (1) mount a subsidy program to offset the concessions being granted by the other countries to their fishing industry, or (2) enjoy the benefits of the other nations' subsidy programs by importing the fish at a lower cost than that incurred domestically. Thus, the country to realize the advantages of a subsidy to fishing is most likely the country in which the final product is marketed rather than necessarily in the country which is granting the subsidy.

There is one final aspect of the Georges Bank haddock fishery that is extremely important. As pointed out above, to achieve the maximum revenue from the resource, the fish must be channeled into the highest value market. Haddock from Georges Bank can be landed fresh in New England and retailed as a fresh fish product— the highest value product form for haddock. However, the same fish landed in any other country likely would have to be marketed in a lower value form, i.e., either as frozen or salted fish, or possibly even as fish meal. It seems to me that this is one of the overriding claims that the U.S. has to the Georges Bank haddock fishery.

Many other interesting dimensions of fishery management remain to be discussed. I have only touched on some of the broad

general economic aspects of fishery management. I hope I have posed this complex problem of fishery management in a meaningful and provocative way. The final success of any management program depends in a large part on industry's acceptance of the basic principles involved and the support and cooperation of industry in drafting a management program that will provide the climate for a viable profitable industry for labor, capital, and management.

COMMENT

THOMAS A. FULHAM

Boston Fish Market Corporation

Following on Dr. Graham's paper, it is quite fitting that Mr. Van Meir should round out the vital subject of the conservation of the fishing resources of Georges Bank by concerning himself with a new, but necessary phase of this whole subject which is the economic aspect. I was quite interested in his quotation attributed to Dr. Martin Burkenroad which he calls "cleverly stated" concerning the management of fisheries. This is probably creative semantics, but I tend to hold a view that if the fisheries are to be of continuous benefit to man, they had better be managed so that they can preserve themselves.

The basis of this whole subject of management starts with the establishment of a sufficient authority; an authority which the author of the paper sees fit to have solely in the realm of the Federal government. With the enactment of the cooperative legislation between the state and Federal governments for the development of state fisheries, I suggest it would be wise to include the state governments in any overall authority governing the management of the fisheries. The possible expansion of fishery territorial waters and new definitions of base lines will probably bring more fishing area under state supervision and direction.

I quite agree with the section of the paper which forecasts a primary increase in the financial yield to a fishing boat operating company as the demand for fish increases and the supply decreases, provided the stock remains unregulated. If we assume further that the stock does become regulated, on an effort basis, serious attempts will have to be made to determine actually what is a unit of effort. We know, at the present time, that an average unit of effort for Boston could be a 120 foot trawler of approximately 700 horse power with a crew of 17 men. An analysis of these vessels in 1965 will show that a satisfactory return will be made, both to the vessel owner and to the fishermen. If we now translate the unit of effort to be a 130 foot stern trawler of 1250 horse power with 13 fishermen aboard we get quite a different picture. I know attempts to define a unit of effort have been made but, as yet, no standard seems to have been determined.

I was more than somewhat confused by the phrase entitled "freedom of entry" as a title for operating under a quota system. Although I am certain that this applies to the fact that man can take the strongest possible economic unit and fish as rapidly as possible, there is nothing very free about having a gate close on you after a short fishing period. I have heard alternate plans under a quota system where the year was divided into 7 or 13 periods. This would appeal to me far more than the one grand slam attempt to catch the allowable quota in one short commercial effort.

There is little that is heart warming to the commercial operator in this document. The prospect is for controlled, licensed fishing units, intermittent operation in an age headed for the concept of the annual wage, and small rewards for companies with an eye to expansion.

I do not agree that under the fishing rights system the catching technology would improve. There would be some variance in proficiency but any unit that survived, would be content to survive, if a small but continuous return could be reasonably guaranteed by the restriction of new units entering the fishery. Soon we would settle into a coma of harmonious mediocrity.

With regard to the management program between nations the author proposes two propositions which, I am sure, would never be supported by the local fisheries. First, the supposition that local fish dealers could enjoy the benefits of the other nations' subsidy programs by importing the fish for less than it likely could be produced domestically. Secondly, as regards the local advantage in fresh fish marketing, I am sure that should, for example, the Canadians continue to be more highly subsidized than the New England fishermen, it would not be long before fresh fish, by modern transportation, could be retailed in New England at a cost less than the same fish could be produced from Boston, Gloucester or New Bedford, so our claim on the Georges Bank haddock on this ground would quickly be dissipated.

At a recent meeting, the International Convention for the Northwest Atlantic Fisheries, which has always been strongly biologically oriented, began discussions on bringing into their consideration the guidance and assistance of economists from the various nations. The decision was brought about, mainly, because conservation measures which have been adopted over the years, especially trawl mesh size regulations, do not seem to be able to keep up with the expansion of fishing power in the attempt to control or to maintain the maximum sustained yield of haddock from Georges Bank. In the light of Mr. Van Meir's paper, the cleavage between biological considerations and economic considerations is still quite pronounced. I am sure that, at some distant point, a common ground to manage the two interests will have to be devised. It is reasonably difficult, however, to formulate a plan which will unite the considerations of preserving the fish for the fish's sake and employing the fish for the sake of consumers.

A very important factor in considering the economics of management is the fact that our local fishery cannot, at the present stage of its development, produce enough fish to meet the demands of either the fresh or frozen fish markets. The recent decision of the Catholic Church to alter its traditional stand on Friday abstinence might temporarily change the supply-demand picture, but this will be quite transitory, due to the fact that, with growing populations, there really is not enough of popular species to go around, so we shall always have to be dependent upon fisheries other than our own to supply even a part of our basic demands. Human tastes being what they are, decimation of specific parts of our fishery populations probably will occur long before these tastes can be altered or regulated.

Fishery economists should take into careful consideration that the popular species of groundfish are no longer a cheap, bulk commodity destined for the table of the low income consumer. The supply picture being what it is, the future pattern of distribution for locally produced fresh fish will be concentrated in the better class restaurants for discerning fish eaters. With this in mind, every effort should be made to devise and utilize the best possible catching, storing, and handling methods in order to eliminate every possible source of detraction from the full economic potential of both the materials used and the products realized.

THE ECONOMICS OF A FISHERY:

THE NEW BEDFORD SCALLOP INDUSTRY

DONALD J. WHITE and CHARLES L. VAUGHN

Boston College

What does the future hold for the New Bedford scallop industry?

Prophecy is a hazardous exercise at best, but some analytical speculation about the future prospects of this important fishery may provide some insights and guides as to the most promising courses of action for the years ahead.

Between 1961 and 1963, the Boston College Bureau of Business Research made a study of sea scallop production. The study was financed by the U.S. Fish and Wildlife Service, Bureau of Commercial Fisheries, and it focused upon scallop production in New Bedford and Nova Scotia.[1]

The study found that Nova Scotia, which did not undertake scalloping operations in a substantial way until after 1956, had by 1962 taken over nearly one-third of what, fortunately, was an expanding United States market. The information in Table 1 shows how things changed between 1956 and 1962:

---

[1]See Richard M. Doherty, G. Paul Draheim, Donald J. White and Charles L. Vaughn, "Economic Study of Sea Scallop Production in the United States and Canada," *Fishery Industrial Research.* U.S. Fish and Wildlife Service, Bureau of Commercial Fisheries, Vol. 2, No. 3, (1965), pp. 57-59.

TABLE 1

IMPORTS OF CANADIAN SCALLOPS RELATED TO
THE DOMESTIC U.S. SUPPLY 1956 and 1962

Year	U.S. Landings	Canadian Imports	Total Landings and Imports	Canadian Imports Relative to the Total	New Bedford Landings	New Bedford Landings Relative to the Total
1956	20.1	1.3	21.3	6.0%	14.2	66%
1962	24.6	11.4	36.0	31.7%	19.3	59%

Source: Richard M. Doherty, G. Paul Draheim, Donald J. White, and Charles L. Vaughn, in U.S. Fish and Wildlife Service, Bureau of Commercial Fisheries, **FISHERY INDUSTRIAL RESEARCH**, Vol. 2, No. 3, 1965, pp. 2-3. Landings figures in Millions of pounds.

In the briefest terms, New Bedford landed 5 million more pounds of scallops in 1962 than in 1956, an increase of 36% in landings, and still served seven per cent *less* of the American market. But, what was worse, the market really did not expand fast enough in this period to take all of these scallops, for prices dropped significantly. In fact, New Bedford received just about the same amount of scallop revenue ($7.9 million) for landings of 19.3 million pounds in 1962 as it had received in 1956 for landings of 14.2 million pounds.[2] Although not too much is known about the market for scallops, the continuing scallop promotional campaign, financed by a deduction from the gross stock of each trip under the terms of the labor agreement between the New Bedford Fishermen's Union and the New Bedford Seafood Producers' Association, probably contributed significantly to preventing a total debacle for New Bedford by 1962.

But what accounted for the fantastic growth of the Nova Scotian scallop industry between 1956 and 1962? The Boston College study found that the Canadians had significant cost advantages over New Bedford. What were these advantages?

1. Canadian governmental subsidies: In addition to low interest loans and accelerated depreciation provisions, the Canadian government provided out-right capital grants of 40 percent of the cost of constructing vessels of 100 gross tons or over beginning in 1961. Under the latter policy, 16 scallop vessels between 92 and 100 feet in length were constructed between October, 1961 and October, 1962.

---

[2] The actual revenue figure for New Bedford for 1956 was $7.7 million.

2. Canadian vessels each fished more intensively; that is, each vessel stayed at sea longer on each trip than did New Bedford vessels. Moreover, Canadian vessels spent less time in port between trips than New Bedford vessels. Both of these factors increased the effective fishing time per vessel per year for Canadian vessels over New Bedford vessels and gave the Canadians more favorable physical productivity ratios.

3. Vessel for vessel, the Canadians used more manpower per unit of capital than did New Bedford without any significant drop in output per man and this contributed to greater productivity per vessel.

4. Pay arrangements for crewmen were more favorable to the owner in Canada than in New Bedford, mainly because, in Canada, dealer-processors owned the vessels and seemed to have some market power to hold down the ex-vessel price on which, under the lay, wage payments to the fishermen were based. In addition, trip expenses (including food) were lower in Canada than in New Bedford. Although annual earnings of scallop fishermen in Canada were well below those in New Bedford, they were nevertheless so much above alternative earnings opportunities in Nova Scotia that scalloping there was regarded as a quite desirable occupation for which manpower supplies were more than adequate.

5. Canadian vessels had a substantial advantage over New Bedford vessels in personal injury insurance costs — Canadian costs in 1960 running on the order of $94 per crewman compared with costs in New Bedford between $300 and $450 per crewman. Though it is not clear how much of this difference is due to differing accident frequency, incidence, and severity as between New Bedford and Canadian operations, it seems clear that the differing legal systems for handling such matters in the two countries exert some influence on these costs. Canadian fishermen are covered by that country's Workmen's Compensation Act which expressly spells out the vessel operator's liability. Fishermen in the United States, including those in New Bedford, are covered by the Jones Act, which subjects the vessel operator to unlimited liability, often determined by jury trial.

These, then, were found to be the major cost factors favoring the Canadian operator. They go far toward explaining how the Canadians, exploiting essentially the same fishing grounds, could so rapidly come to rival the New Bedford producers.

The advent of this Canadian competition found the New Bedford scallop industry in relatively far better shape than any other part of the New England offshore fishing industry. The scalloper fleet was relatively modern, well maintained, and manned by capable captains and crewmen. Nonetheless, the Canadian bid for the U.S. market measurably increased the pressures on New Bedford operators and crewmen to increase their efficiency if they were to hold their own, let alone advance their position.

The Boston College scallop study underscored this situation. While the study documented the relatively fine physical condition of the scallop fleet, it warned that the New Bedford scallop industry faced further shrinkage unless it took steps to diminish New Bedford's cost handicaps vis-a-vis Nova Scotia. The study suggested that regardless of what happened to the productivity of the scallop resource base—a subject we shall return to later—New Bedford interests should explore certain ways to increase vessel productivity and to cut costs , particularly insurance costs.[3] The study praised New Bedford's efforts to strengthen the scallop market through a solid advertising and promotion program and it noted with satisfaction the success of New Bedford interests in inducing Canadian sea scallop buyers and packers to join in contributing financially to the advertising program.

What happened to the industry after 1962?[4]

1. The productivity of the scallop resource base declined. Scallops became scarce on Georges Bank, and notwithstanding a shift of fishing effort to banks off New Jersey and Virginia, total landings of scallops declined.[5] Total U.S. landings plus imports from

---

[3] Specifically, the study suggested New Bedford vessel owners and the New Bedford Fishermen's Union explore ways to attain the largest catch per year per vessel consistent with the maintenance of quality, by maximizing actual fishing time per year per vessel. Admittedly, this would not be easy, for it would involve more flexible crewing arrangements so that individual fishermen might have no less time home per trip while insuring fuller vessel utilization. It would also involve slightly larger crews per vessel and longer trips from dock to dock. The study stressed that it did not intend that the fishermen give up any of the favorable conditions achieved through constructive collective bargaining. The study rather stressed that the parties try to safeguard these conditions while at the same time improving vessel productivity. The study also emphasized the need to investigate the possibility of achieving some sort of workmen's compensation approach to the insurance problem as well as the need to concentrate upon reducing accident-related work losses. The further extension of fleet wide cooperative purchasing arrangements was also suggested as a way to cut the cost of trip expenditures.

[4] All data below unless otherwise indicated are from the U.S. Fish and Wildlife Service.

[5] The magnitude of this shift is indicated by two facts: a) between June and November, 1965, inclusive, approximately 300,000 pounds of the New Bedford landings came from the Georges Banks area and four million pounds from the region south of New York City; and b) landings at New York and south increased from about two million pounds during the first eleven months of 1964 to seven million pounds in the comparable period of 1965. There are indications, however, that scallopers are returning to Georges Banks because of the limited resource available in the mid-Atlantic area.

Canada dropped from 36 million pounds in 1962 to 32.5 million pounds in 1964.

2. In the face of this development, New Bedford and Canada fared quite differently. Canada increased its landings and increased its exports to the United States from 11.4 million pounds in 1962 to 15.5 million pounds in 1964. This raised Canada's share of the American market from 31.7 per cent in 1962 to 47.7 per cent in 1964 —a share that promises to be easily continued or surpassed in 1965. Please keep in mind that the Canadians work about the same resources and share the same difficulties in that regard as New Bedford producers encounter.

3. New Bedford landings, on the other hand, fell from 19.3 million pounds in 1962 to 12.9 million pounds in 1964, a drop of 33 per cent. New Bedford's share of the American market fell from 53 per cent in 1962 to 39 per cent in 1964. Since imports through September, 1965, are not much below last year while 1965 New Bedford landings have been running around 2.5 million pounds under 1964, New Bedford's share of the American market promises to reach a record low this year. [6]

As might be expected, these developments have had the effect of reducing the importance of New Bedford as a scallop producing center. Fortunately, however, a number of factors have kept this turn of events from hurting individual vessel owners and fishermen in the port:

First: Due perhaps in no small measure to the enlightened promotional efforts of New Bedford interests in cooperation with Canadian producers, the market for scallops has been continually strengthened.[7] For example, in 1964, New Bedford interests received $7 million for scallop landings of 12.9 million pounds, only $900,000, or 12 per cent, less than the revenue received for landings of 19.3 million pounds in 1962. And it appears now that New Bedford interests may receive as much as $500,000 more in 1965 than they received in 1964 for landings that promise to be upwards of 2.5 million pounds under 1964.

6 Total imports through September, 1965, were 12.2 million. For the same period in 1964 they were 12.6 million.

7 It should be noted, however, that knowledge of the scallop market is limited. It appears that the market is segmented; that is, the demand of such institutional buyers as restaurants and hotels is considerably less elastic than the consumer demand at the retail level, especially the demand serviced by chain stores. Hence it appears that efforts to broaden the institutional market which would offer higher prices per pound would pay great dividends. In any case, a careful market study which provides a detailed configuration of demand for scallops could be of great value to the industry.

Second: Due in considerable measure to the strength of the market for, and the availability of supplies of,other types of fish landed in the port, most prominently yellowtail flounder, many vessels have shifted out of scalloping so revenue per scallop vessel has advanced substantially. Between 1962 and 1964, the number of vessels fishing year round for scallops dropped from 47 to 35, or 25 per cent, and the total number fishing for scallops, both year round and seasonally, dropped from 60 to 43, or 28 per cent.

Third: There has been some shift of landings to New Jersey ports, and some increase of landings at Rhode Island ports. Many of these landings have come from New Bedford vessels which might otherwise have landed at New Bedford if there had not been the shift to exploiting resources nearer to New Jersey and Virginia. Aside from possible inconvenience to captain and crews, this shift has not hurt New Bedford operators although it obviously has cut into New Bedford's marketing significance. The shift has had one other effect, however, which is not so salutary, for it appears that buyers do not regard scallops from these latter sources as being as good as those from Georges and the price paid for them is less than that brought by scallops from Georges. It is little satisfaction to us that we foresaw some three years ago that Canada might soon overtake New Bedford as a supplier of the American scallop market. The gratifying thing is that the strength of the scallop market, together with opportunities in fishing for other species, have made relative prosperity possible for those who have remained in the New Bedford scallop industry. This is not exactly the spectacle of riding to the graveyard in a gold plated hearse, but it does seriously raise the question as to whether New Bedford's heyday in scallops has passed. The peak year for revenue was 1959, when 18.8 million pounds of scallops brought in $9.1 million. The year 1964 actually fell behind 1952—when 12.1 million pounds of scallops sold for $7.2 million.

The evidence seems fairly clear that the number of men and the number of vessels employed on a relatively prosperous basis in the New Bedford scallop industry in coming years is likely to be less than in the past, and probably substantially less than in past peak years. But this does not mean scallops cannot continue to be a substantial revenue producer for New Bedford. Steps that might implement such an outcome might include the following:

1. Continued expansion of the biological study of the sea scallop to increase scientific understanding of this resource so that its management can become more effective. Needless to say, perhaps, is that this study and certainly the management problem should be explored jointly with Canada, since Canada is a vital factor in the American industry. In so far as possible, other countries should also be brought into the picture. One specific type of study should be the sizes of scallops in catches so that gear research can be conducted to permit their control. (Admittedly, this type of effort is expensive.)

2. Continued cooperation between Canadian and New Bedford interests on market development, though the Canadians might frankly acknowledge their increased stake in this market and increase their contribution to the intensive development of it. As recent events disclose, the problem is not so much one of increasing the volume of sales as it is discovering and exploiting highest possible value outlets per unit product. New Bedford's marketing and advertising representatives realize this and are already so orienting their marketing efforts.[8]

3. Exploration of the possibility to use the new U.S. Fishing Vessel Subsidy Act to New Bedford's advantage. Obviously, the problem is not to expand the fleet, but to upgrade it even further. In view of the Canadian subsidy program, U.S. officials ought to take a sympathetic view of New Bedford interests to use the American act to benefit this country's industry.[9] Great longer-term benefits could be obtained if governmental fishery officials in the U.S. and in Canada, working with an advisory committee drawn from the industry in their respective countries, could sit down and try to work out reasonable capital assistance policies for the future which would minimize possible capital wastage and recognize some fair basis for the respective interests of the two nations in the exploitation of scallop resources.

4. A frontal assault on the insurance cost problem in New Bedford. This matter has been the subject of conversation, comment, and fragmentary attack for a long time.[10] Not only should the indus-

[8] The 1964-65 Report of Scallop Advertising by McPartland-Bidwell Inc., which represents the industry for advertising and public relations, describes in some detail how advertising and public relations efforts have already been shifted to identify scallops with a higher priced market.

[9] It should be recognized that the Canadian subsidy program was designed to stimulate ship-building in general: a side-effect was the building of scallop vessels.

[10] See, for example: Donald J. White, "What are the Keys to Continued Scallop Prosperity at New Bedford," *Maine Coast Fisherman,* November, 1959, pp. 9 and 16.

try redouble its efforts to deal with it, but also the U.S. Fish and Wildlife Service, either on an in-house or contract basis, should seek the most expert probe of the matter and should cooperate with the industry to implement resulting recommendations.

5. In the final analysis, no matter how cooperative governmental and private interests in the U.S. and Canada may become—and there should be far more such cooperation than now—still, the areas will remain competitive, so that New Bedford interests must concentrate on seeking to constantly improve manning and vessel utilization practices, in ways akin to those suggested in the Boston College Scallop Study, to achieve lowest possible costs.

There is, then, no reason why the future of the New Bedford scallop industry needs to be regarded as bleak. It may not be possible to recapture past glories, but the future can be bright. That new ways of thinking may be required, and novel efforts may be involved is only one way of saying that this industry, no less than nearly all others in an era of rapid change, must seize the initiative to turn problems into accomplishment.

COMMENT

OCTAVIO A. MODESTO

Seafood Producers Association

After listening to such a good and complete analysis of the New Bedford fishing industry, it is rather difficult to expand on the subject.

I noticed a reference to the 1962 price drop in scallops. The situation was a serious one and it hit the boat owner in their most vulnerable spot—the pocket! To overcome this, the Seafood Council went to work. Further assistance came from the Federal government and the Bureau of Commercial Fisheries, particularly. The chain stores also helped to make people aware that scallops were a particularly good buy at the time. Consequently, by the increased efforts of all concerned, more and more people were convinced of the high nutritional value of scallops, the delightful taste and ease in preparation. This particular blitz promotion is one of the important factors for the expanding and holding of a good market and steady demand.

As indicated in the preceeding paper, scallop prices have risen to more than twice that low figure and are selling steadily. Not only was the demand increased for domestic scallops, but the American public has also absorbed the Nova Scotian scallops in stride.

The reference to the Canadian operating costs and the New Bedford vessel owners costs is quite significant. This is particularly prominent and painful in the amount of insurance paid by our New Bedford boats compared to the Canadian boats. It is startling that New Bedford boat owners must pay four times the premium for approximately the same coverage. We have brought this to the attention of our legislators and currently there is a study being made of ways to alleviate this condition. It is our opinion, as well as that of others, that the antiquated Jones Act is in part responsible for some of this high cost. A reasonable amendment to the Jones Act should be adopted. We feel that such an instrument could be fairer to the boat owners without taking away or reducing any just benefits due the crewmen. We are insistent that suits be confined to injury aboard the vessel.

Canada has, of late, been exceeding our scallops production for various reasons. Our boat owners, up until very recently, have had to pay full price of about $150,000 per scalloper. Today the cost is even greater, and the Fishing Fleet Improvement Act of 1964 has not yet had the desired effect and assistance in our port. The Canadian competitor is heavily subsidized. Furthermore, the Canadian is not restricted to size of boat or number of crew. By Union contract, the New Bedford boat owners cannot sail with a crew in excess of twelve. Up until 1961, the contract had implied that eight maximum fishing days would constitute a trip. The estimate was that each man was capable of producing approximately 250 pounds every forty-eight hours. This resulted in 11,000 to 12,000 pound catches, while the Canadians were fishing beyond this period of time, with larger vessels and more crew. Since the Canadians had no limit, while our vessels, in living up to the contract, were bringing in this small amount per man, the Canadians were bringing in far in excess of this amount with, as pointed out, larger boats and greater number of men. These large catches by the Canadians, as well as their subsidy and encouragement by the Canadian government, no doubt were influencing factors in increased investments in Canadian scallop vessels. The New Bedford vessels have always worked on a theory that a shorter trip would result in a better and fresher product. Then too, the contract between management and labor sets a limit on the number of fishing days and I believe the Canadians do not adhere to any set limit of time or catch. Despite all these factors, our boats have been very successful and are well kept up and newer ones are constantly entering the fleet.

It is interesting to note, in one of the recommendations, that the management of the scallop fishery by Canadian and New Bedford interests be considered. While we could jointly manage the market, promotion and distribution of the product, it would be somewhat difficult at present to manage a resource that is the property of one as much as the other. It has been pointed out by oceanographic scientists that this would present a problem, and the problem would be to determine who would have the responsibility, how much responsibility would be had and where the responsibility would start or stop. Then, too, if this were a reality, how could we deny a third party, or others, from coming into the development or farm area? We might find ourselves in the unenviable and embarrassing position of having sown crops only to have some greedy onlooker send in a fleet of boats and take advantage of our good nature. I doubt that we are ready for such action, although I do not doubt that there is an ultimate need for development of such an idea.

We are in agreement with one suggestion—that concerning the Canadian contributions. As pointed out, they are now contributing partially to our marketing efforts and sometime ago we met with their representatives and indicated that they should re-evaluate the results and consider matching our contribution. This is still under consideration by them.

One factor not directly shown in these figures, but still a great economic factor, is the necessity for improving our personnel. We are faced with a manpower shortage. No doubt new and additional boats will continue to enter our fleet. Up until now the only training a scallop fisherman received was to be permitted or invited to go aboard a vessel to make a trip and see if he could acclimate himself and to learn principally by observation. Fortunately, after several tries, we were able to launch an OJT Fishermen's Training Program in New Bedford for draggers. While these men are learning limited skills in a loft and then, after a period of time, take trips on draggers, they can very easily adapt themselves to the scalloping operations. The vessels, scallopers and draggers, are quite similar. The gear, of course, varies and the areas fished will vary. There is one particular and difficult technique in scalloping which would be a difficult thing for a man to learn ashore. I refer to the "shucking" or the opening of scallops. This is done in the primitive manner by opening the shells with knives and cutting out the edible part of the scallop. Sometime ago we discussed the possibility of developing an automatic shucking device but there has been no progress with this mechanical technique.

Why has it been difficult to attract young people into the industry to become fishermen? One of the things that we can think of is that the fisherman is away from home from five to nine days. He lives in close quarters with other members of the crew, and in his leisure time aboard does not get into his car and take his family for a drive or go visiting; he is on call twenty-four hours a day, if an emergency arises. The attractive part to these individuals is that scallop fishermen earn good wages. When one considers the amount of time spent at work and away from their families, you will agree with me that they are not the least overpaid.

Recently, I noted an article in the *Canadian Fisherman* admitted an increasing manpower shortage in their fishery. They, as we, have no skilled fishermen to fill the gap but have developed a training program which embraces not only the actual fishing, but navigation and marine engines as well, at the Newfoundland College of Fisheries. It would behoove our fishing industry to assess our program and to institute a similar program and expand any existing program to meet our current need for fishery personnel.

In conclusion I would say that our greatest needs are:

1. Stepped up scientific research and development of our scallop resources.

2. More economic relief and assistance from the Federal government, particularly on excessive insurance costs.

3. Improved gear, techniques and automation.

4. Schools to develop fishermen.

The last is particularly important, because no matter how good a vessel we have, how efficient and modern the gear may be, and how wealthy a resource, a vessel still must have men to operate it.

INDEX

INDEX

L

Labor force, 11-13, 135-46
    Canadian, 16, 142
    mobility, 144
    need for improvement, 222-23
    skill mix, 138-41, 145
    sources of, 143-45
    unionization, 16, 101, 131, 139, 221
    wages, 7, 12, 123-24, 128, 137, 138-40, 145, 215
    See also Captains
              Costs
              Fishermen
Labor problems, 11-13, 135-46, 222-23
Lampe, Harlan C., 6-7, 13-4, 45, 45n, 61, 62, 179, 184n, 193-95
Landings, 7-8, 22, 46-8, 53-7, 65-83, 147-77, 197-201, 218
    See also Individual species
"Lay," 6, 8, 12, 50, 123-24, 123n (def.), 132
    Canadian, 16, 215
    Italian, 100, 101
Least squares analysis. *See* Statistical analysis—least squares
Legislation, 16-7, 25, 26, 209
    See also Individual Acts (Fishing Fleet Improvement Act, Jones Act, etc.)
Lenten Season. *See* Religious influences
Lynch, E. J., 87n, 96n, 107, 107n, 131n

M

McConnell, Joseph L., 92n, 99, 99n
McPartland-Bidwell, Inc. (Report of Scallop Advertising), 219n
Mackeral, 148, 172
Management and regulation, Fisheries, 13-5, 152, 175, 197-211, 197 (def.)
    alternatives, 14-5, 205-09
    co-operative, 13, 15, 197-98, 210-11, 219, 220, 222
    federal, 20, 197. 209

    freedom of entry, 15, 205-07, 210
    monopolistic exploitation, 15, 206-07
    quota system, 15, 205-08, 210
    state, 209
Marketing of fish, 8, 16, 31-44, 46, 62, 65-83, 208, 211, 214, 216, 217, 219, 220, 222
    processing, 46, 47, 66
    wholesale and retail trade, 46-7, 76-8
    See also Individual species
Markets for fish, 4-8, 13-4, 45-63, 65-83, 179-95
    geographical distribution, 7-8, 70-2, 74-5
    methods of research, 7-8, 66-9
    See also Imports
              Individual species
Massachusetts Department of Corporations and Taxation, 97
Massachusetts, University of. Department of Agriculture and Food Products, 83
Maximum sustainable yield. *See* Yield, Sustainable
Menhaden, 20, 23, 169
Michigan State University. Consumer Budget Panel, 35, 43, 54
Miernyk, W. K., 105, 105n, 106, 106n, 107n, 109, 109n
Miller, Morton M., 12, 135

Models, Fishing industry:
    least-squares single equation, 41, 41n
    of haddock market, 6-7, 45-63
    population, 13-4, 179-95
    two-fishery, 13-4, 179-95
        —biological, 180-81
        —economic, 181-92

Modesto, Octavio A., 220
Monopolistic exploitation. *See* Management and regulation, Fisheries—monopolistic exploitation
Mortality rates, Fish, 180-83, 185, 190-91
Muir, Allan T., 142n

230

N

Narragansett (stern trawler), 11
Nash, Darrel A., 5-6, 7, 31, 40-1,
43-4
New Bedford Fisherman's Union, 214,
216n
New Bedford fleet, 50, 101, 221
New Bedford scallop industry, 15-6,
213-23
New Bedford Seafood Producers As-
sociation, 16, 214
New Brunswick Department of Fish-
eries, 11
New England Fish Exchange, 66
New England fishing industry, 3-4, 9,
15-6, 19-27, 45-63, 120, 131 (def.),
173, 174-77
    See also Fleets—New England
Newfoundland College of Fisheries,
223
Newport (R. I.) fleet, 119-32
North Atlantic fishery, 13, 20, 147-77
Norton, Virgil J., 12, 31n, 135

O

Ocean Perch. *See* Redfish
Officers. *See* Captains
Olson, Fred, 31n
O'Rourke, Hugh F., 8, 81
Oysters, 20

P

Pesticides. *See* Pollution problems
Point Judith Fisherman's Co-opera-
tive, 121, 131
Point Judith (R. I.) fleet, 119-32
Pollock, 8, 65, 73-5, 148, 171
Pollution problems, 21, 24
    pesticides, 21, 24, 25
Population, Fish. *See* Supply of fish
    Individual species
Processing. *See* Marketing—processing
Production function, 8-11, 87-118
    See also Cobb - Douglas Produc-
        tion Function
        Demand

Productivity, 119, 137, 205
    marginal, 136-37, 140, 145
    of labor, 110-11, 137, 137n, 221
    of vessels, 110-12, 216
    See also Vessels—utilization
        Technology and techno-
            logical change
Profits, 92-9, 107, 117, 127-30, 205-
07
    See also Production function
        Rate of return
        Revenue
Profit sharing. *See* "Lay"

Q

Quota system. *See* Management and
    regulation, Fisheries—quota system

R

Rate of return, 7-11, 50-3, 87-118,
119-32
    Agriculture — Forestry — Fishing;
        All Manufacturing, 96
Recruitment (fish). *See* Supply of fish
    —recruitment
Red Hake, 23, 148, 152, 167-69
Reder, Melvin W., 140, 140n
Redfish (Ocean Perch), 20, 23, 39,
148, 159-60, 167-69
Regulation, Fisheries. *See* Manage-
    ment and regulation, Fisheries
Religious influences, 7, 46, 53-5, 58,
63, 79, 81, 82-3, 211
Resource base. *See* Supply of fish
Retail trade. *See* Marketing—whole-
    sale and retail trade
Revenue, 6-7, 45-63, 91-2, 100, 107,
110, 124, 185, 204, 206-07
Reynolds, Lloyd G., 144, 144n
Rhode Island University. Department
    of Food and Resource Economics,
121
Rosen, Sumner, 105, 105n, 106, 106n,
107n, 109, 109n
Russian fishing industry, 119, 155,
157, 167

V

Van Camp Seafood Company, 22, 23
Van Meir, Lawrence W., 14-5, 106,
 106n, 120-21, 123, 197, 209-11
Van Tassel, Roger C., 117
Vaughn, Charles L., 15, 15n, 16, 101,
 213, 213n
Vessels:
 characteristics, 9, 88, 105-09, 115,
  122
 cost of operation, 9, 101, 125,
  132, 216n
 depreciation, 10, 92, 125-27
 earnings, 108
 geographical distribution, 88-91
 production function, 8-11, 87-118
 rate of return, 9-10, 51-2, 103-07,
  120-21
 trawlers, 10-11, 25, 119-32
  —side, 10 (def.), 11, 50-3
  —stern, 3-4, 10 (def.), 11,
   26, 50-3
 utilization, 109, 109n, 110, 114n,
  137, 137n, 215, 216n, 221-22
 value, measures of, 91, 92, 97,
  114-16, 126-28
 See also Equipment
  Fleets
  Subsidies, Construction

W

Wages. *See* Captains—earnings
  Fishermen—wages
  "Lay"
Ward, George, 11n
White, Donald J., 3, 3n, 4, 15, 15n,
 16, 213, 213n, 219n
Whiting. *See* Silver Hake
Wholesale trade. *See* Marketing—
  wholesale and retail trade
Wilkinson, John M., 13, 174
Woods Hole Biological Laboratory,
 199
Working, E. J., 41n, 42
Workmen's Compensation Act, Can-
 adian, 215

Y

Yield effort curve, 152
Yield on capital. *See* Rate of return
Yield, Sustainable, 13, 14-5, 123, 152-
 73, 175-76, 195, 201-04, 207
 See also Effort, Fishing
  Individual species

Z

Zellner, Arnold, 179, 197, 197n, 198